DRUGS IN SCOTLAND: MEETING THE CHALLENGE

Report of Ministerial Drugs Task Force

Chairman: The Rt Hon The Lord Fraser of Carmyllie QC
Minister of State, The Scottish Office

The Scottish Office Home and Health Department
St Andrew's House
Edinburgh

October 1994

CONTENTS

FOREWORD BY THE RT HON IAN LANG MP SECRETARY OF STATE FOR SCOTLAND

Effective action against drugs is one of the greatest challenges facing Scotland today. Drug misuse damages, and all too often destroys, young lives. It disrupts families and communities. It spawns crime and violence. It exacts a high price on the whole of society.

The growing concern about the serious nature of drug misuse in Scotland, and the need to ensure that our response was as well directed and integrated as it could be, led me to set up the Drugs Task Force under the chairmanship of Lord Fraser. In pursuing its remit the Drugs Task Force has carried out a thorough review of the current arrangements for combating drug misuse and has produced a full programme of action for tackling this complex and difficult problem.

There is no simple solution to the problem of drug misuse. We need to harness the energies, commitment and professionalism of all the agencies which have a role to play, within a framework which provides clear direction and leadership. I am grateful to the Task Force for their work in producing this report which provides a comprehensive and constructive strategy for action. I commend the report to the many statutory and non-statutory agencies who are already working diligently in the field. I believe there is a real desire in communities all over Scotland to turn the tide of drug misuse.

The Task Force report provides a lead: the challenge for us all is to respond with the necessary vigour and enthusiasm, which will enable us to see a dramatic reduction in the misuse of drugs in Scotland.

IAN LANG

Scottish Ministerial Drugs Task Force Membership

Mrs J Barlow, Senior Manager, Aberlour Child Care Trust, Stirling

Miss L Barrie, General Manager, Tayside Health Board

Dr H A Bowyer, Consultant in Public Health Medicine, Borders Health Board

Mr J Chant, Director of Social Work, Lothian Regional Council

Mrs A D'Mello, Co-ordinator, West Fife Community Drugs Project

Mr E Goodwin, Detective Sergeant, Lothian and Borders Police

Mr A Johnstone, Rector, Harris Academy, Dundee

Dr D Jolliffe, formerly GP and part-time Prison Medical Officer, recently appointed Medical Adviser to the Scottish Prison Service

Dr D H Kennedy, Consultant Physician, Department of Infection and Tropical Medicine, Ruchill Hospital, Glasgow

Mr D Liddell, Co-ordinator, Scottish Drugs Forum

Mr J D Lowe, Crown Agent, Crown Office, Edinburgh

Mr A W Ramsay, Adviser in Health Education, Strathclyde Regional Council

Dr A J Tannahill, General Manager, Health Education Board for Scotland

Mr J Welsh, Assistant Chief Constable, Strathclyde Police

Mr A Williams, Chief Administrative Pharmaceutical Officer, Grampian Health Board and Chairman, Grampian Drug Liaison Committee

Mr R Winter, Depute Director of Social Work, Strathclyde Regional Council

EXECUTIVE SUMMARY

Drug misuse is a serious and escalating problem in Scotland. For the individual, drugs can provide a quick boost, but at the risk of prosecution, damage to health, a drift into destitution and, in a significant and worrying number of cases, even death. For the families of misusers - their parents, spouses and children - drugs can mean anguish, social conflict and break-up, and poverty. For the wider community, drug misuse imposes heavy demands on services, is a major contributor to crime levels, gives rise to public health hazards and, in relation to drug trafficking, is closely associated with organised crime, intimidation and violence.

The most commonly abused drug in Scotland is cannabis. Other so called "recreational" drugs, such as Ecstasy, are widely used by young people and are a focus of growing public concern. A particular feature of the Scottish drugs scene is the high incidence of injecting drug misuse. This is especially harmful to health because unsafe injecting practices can lead to the transmission of HIV and hepatitis and can give rise to other problems such as abscesses and septicaemia.

Injecting drug misuse is a particular problem in some of the peripheral housing schemes of the Scottish cities, but there are also significant drug misuse problems in the smaller Scottish towns and in rural areas. "Recreational" drug misuse is very widespread, geographically and socially, throughout Scotland. A general shift in social attitudes towards drugs, especially among young people, is required.

Drug misuse is therefore a major social problem which society as a whole needs to tackle. It is not a problem which can be left to the NHS, the social work services and the police, though they have important roles to play. The response needs to be multi-agency and multi-disciplinary. Vigorous, imaginative, co-ordinated action is required at local and Scottish level.

The Drugs Task Force, consisting of experts from the statutory and voluntary sectors led by the Minister of State, Lord Fraser, has conducted a comprehensive review of the efforts to tackle drug misuse in Scotland, and the following are its key conclusions.

(i)   Much more emphasis should be given to efforts to reduce the demand for drugs. Pilot community drug action schemes should be set up with a particular focus on the development of alternative activities which seek to engage young people at a time in their lives when they are attracted by excitement and risk. Social work departments and the voluntary sector child care organisations should incorporate drugs prevention activity in their work with children and young people. The Health Education Board for Scotland should lead in developing innovative prevention work at the national level.

(ii)   In the schools, new drug prevention packages should be developed for the under 10s and over 14s. Schools should be given guidance on the development of a comprehensive drug policy. The Inspectorate of Schools should seek to stimulate increased activity where necessary, disseminating good practice, and ensuring that a consistent approach is taken throughout the country.

(iii)   There should be a review of the effectiveness of various types of drugs services, leading to advice at national level on which type of service, or which combination of services, is likely to suit which type of misuser.

(iv)   Substitute prescribing has an important part to play in tackling drug misuse, within a structured framework of services. More specific guidelines on the prescribing of substitute drugs should be drawn up.

(v)   The community drug problem services in Scotland should be further developed with a view to achieving more referrals from and to generic social work services; providing additional support to, and obtaining the assistance of, the families of drug misusers; and reaching drug misusers at an earlier point in their drug careers.

(vi)   In dealing with drug-misusing offenders, a range of options should be available to the prosecuting authorities and the courts for deployment according to the circumstances of the case. Non-custodial disposals linked to programmes which seek to tackle drug misuse may be suitable in some cases, particularly in dealing with young offenders or those who are seriously trying to overcome their drug misuse problems. Work in developing such programmes should be taken forward as a priority.

(vii)   Recent initiatives taken by the Scottish Prison Service to tackle drug misuse in prisons are to be commended. This work now needs to be consolidated and taken forward through the development of reduction to abstinence and education programmes for long-term prisoners and the regular training of prison medical staff. Consideration should be given to the piloting of throughcare arrangements which seek to ensure that a prisoner who has become drug free while in prison remains so on his release into the community.

(viii) Drug Action Teams should be set up to lead and co-ordinate local efforts to tackle drug misuse. These teams, which should be based on health board areas, should consist of very senior people from the local agencies concerned. They should draw up, by autumn 1995, strategic plans for tackling drug misuse. Thereafter they will be responsible for driving the plan and securing its delivery. Each team should be supported by a drugs development officer and be able to refer to a wider group - the drugs forum - which will bring together a wide range of community-level experience.

(ix)   A Scottish committee on the misuse of drugs, reporting to the Secretary of State, should be set up to advise on policy, priorities and strategic planning.

Following is a full list of the Task Force's recommendations.

INFORMATION

1.   There is scope for improvements to be made in the collection of information about drug misuse. Progress can best be made by a continuous process of seeking to improve the availability of reliable information, concentrating on what is required for policy development or the delivery of services. This should be taken forward by the proposed Scottish advisory committee (para 2.12).

2.   Consideration should be given to extending the Scottish Drug Misuse Database to include all agency contacts between drug misusers and drug misuse services rather than just the first contact - the current arrangement - while maintaining the anonymity of the information collected (para 2.10).

3.   Social work authorities should ensure that those responsible for assessment across the full range of social work services are alert to

the possibility that drug misuse may be a contributing factor. Authorities should review their arrangements for recording the incidence of drug misuse at the point of referral for social work services with a view to ensuring that the information collected is comprehensive and reliable (para 2.11).

4. The Scottish Office should take steps to ensure that a suitable research programme is developed and sustained (para 3.36).

PREVENTION

5. The Scottish Office should continue to support, and participate in, mass media campaigns at GB level, providing that they are relevant to Scottish circumstances (para 3.4).

6. Priority should be given to the development of preventive work targeted on groups of young people who because of their environment or other factors are particularly vulnerable to drug misuse pressures. The Health Education Board for Scotland (HEBS) and The Scottish Office should determine how this is to be taken forward, if necessary deflecting resources from The Scottish Office's drugs publicity budget (para 3.8).

7. Local authority social work departments and the voluntary sector child care organisations should incorporate drugs prevention activity in their work with children and young people. Their efforts in this direction should be co-ordinated with local and national health and education initiatives (para 3.14).

8. High level co-ordination of policy on drug prevention at national level should be carried out by the proposed Scottish advisory committee. At local level the proposed Drug Action Teams should develop prevention strategies for their areas which are consistent with national policy and aimed at complementing and building on the work undertaken by HEBS and local agencies (para 3.15).

9. If the peer-led education approach being tried in various Scottish projects proves successful, it should be developed (para 3.18).

10. Pilot community drug action schemes should be developed in a number of areas with a view to determining whether such an initiative could be applied successfully on a wider basis (para 3.38).

In particular, these pilot schemes should pursue the development of alternative activities which seek to engage young people at a time in their lives when they are attracted by excitement and risk (para 4.31).

11. Local authorities should ensure that social workers preparing reports for Children's Hearings or supervising children in care are alert to the possibility that a child may be experimenting with drugs or other substances, and that the misuse of drugs and other substances is routinely monitored to ensure that children in care who have problems in this respect get the help they need at the earliest opportunity (para 3.31).

SCHOOLS AND COLLEGES

12. There is a need for regular information on the prevalence of drug misuse among school-age children in order to inform the planning and development of drug prevention measures in schools (para 3.23).

13. The Scottish Office Education Department should issue guidance for all schools in Scotland stressing the importance of drugs prevention education and the need to continue to emphasise this within the syllabus (para 3.24).

14. Within their responsibilities for school inspection work generally, Her Majesty's Inspectorate of Schools should have regard to how schools are tackling drug prevention education with a view to stimulating increased activity where this is shown to be necessary, disseminating good practice and ensuring that a consistent approach is taken throughout the country (para 3.25).

15. The Scottish Office Education Department should develop new drug prevention packages for use in primary schools, focusing on children in the under-10 age group, and on senior secondary pupils in the 15-18 age group (para 3.26).

16. The Scottish Office Education Department should issue policy guidance to ensure that a consistent approach is adopted regarding non- educationists who deliver drugs education in schools (para 3.27).

17. The Scottish Office Education Department should issue guidance to

schools, school boards and parent/teacher associations on the development of a comprehensive drug policy and what this should cover (para 3.28).

18. The Scottish Office should issue guidance to all further and higher education institutions in Scotland on the issues which should be covered in a drugs strategy for these bodies (para 3.34).

19. The Association of Chief Police Officers in Scotland and the Association of Directors of Education in Scotland should co-operate in developing training packages for police officers engaged in school liaison work (para 3.35).

SERVICES

20. Proposals for crisis-intervention centres in Aberdeen and Dundee should be developed as quickly as possible (para 4.3).

21. Future service development must be based on a systematic and comprehensive assessment of the nature, extent and distribution of need. This assessment should be carried out by both health boards and social work departments reporting to the area Drug Action Team (para 4.4).

22. The proposed Scottish advisory committee should establish a sub-group of experts to advise on the effectiveness of various types of provision, including advice on what type of service, or combination of services, suits which type of misuser (para 4.6).

23. The proposed Drug Action Teams should take the lead in ensuring that arrangements are in place locally to monitor the extent to which services are meeting the needs of drug misusers. Drug Action Teams should stimulate the development of services; and they should ensure that the local range of services is subject to systematic review (para 4.8).

24. The proposed Scottish advisory committee should take stock of initiatives undertaken in developing community-based services with a view to developing, funding and evaluating further pilot projects and disseminating information on the most effective and worthwhile approaches (para 4.11).

25. The Community Drug Problem Service model for providing services to drug misusers should be further developed with a view to

achieving more referrals from and to generic social work services; providing additional support to, and obtaining the assistance of, the families of drug misusers; and reaching drug misusers at an earlier point in their drug careers (para 4.21).

26. More specific guidelines on the prescribing of substitute drugs should be drawn up. In addition, independent and objective monitoring of those Scottish drug services which incorporate substitute prescribing should be conducted with a view to further identifying good practice in the delivery of services, including an assessment of effectiveness in controlling and changing drug use behaviour (para 4.23).

27. GPs have a key role to play in the treatment of drug misusers and the Scottish advisory committee should keep under close review action and support for GPs at both local and national level (para 4.26).

28. The Scottish Office should pursue with the Deans of the Medical Schools how enhanced training in dealing with drug misuse might be provided during the undergraduate training of medical students (para 4.28).

29. The agencies employing outreach workers should establish clear objectives and standards of practice for outreach workers and ensure that they are well supported at management level (para 4.30).

30. The Scottish Office should issue guidance for local authorities and licensing boards to bring to the attention of the organisers of "rave" events. This should deal with appropriate levels of stewarding, paramedic staff, "chill out" areas and free accessible water supplies, and information on sensible behaviour and harm minimisation issues surrounding drug use (para 4.33). The Scottish Office, in consultation with the police, local authorities and other relevant interests, should examine the extent to which it might be practicable and useful for model licensing conditions reflecting these areas of concern to be prepared for use by local authorities and licensing boards according to circumstances pertaining in their areas (para 4.34).

31. Needle and syringe exchange schemes have clearly demonstrated their worth and following careful consideration of the Drugs Task Force's views the Lord Advocate has agreed to an increase from 10 to 15 in the number of sets of equipment which an injector may obtain during the second and subsequent visit to an exchange (providing the quantity issued on the previous occasion is returned safely for disposal). In building on the concept of outreach work in

rural areas some carefully selected schemes involving exchange staff making home visits to selected injectors in rural areas should be piloted on a trial basis with a view to considering whether the practice might be adopted more widely (para 4.40).

32. There is considerable potential for pharmacists to play an even greater role in "frontline" services to drug misusers. Health boards should consider how best this can be developed (para 4.41).

33. All female drug misusers, particularly pregnant women and women with children, should have access to regular, sensitive counselling, support and information (para 4.43).

34. Drug Action Teams should examine the need for women-only residential provision (which would enable women to remain with their children if they so wish) in their areas (para 4.44).

35. The agencies concerned should review their services for women drug misusers (including child care needs) and, in particular, consult their women clients for their views on the services offered and encourage them to be involved in the long term monitoring and evaluation of service provision with the aim of developing a more attractive service to women drug misusers (para 4.45).

36. Service providers should ensure that their services are "user-friendly" to members of the ethnic minorities and that they are capable of recognising and addressing possible barriers to the effective provision of services to those who need them (para 4.46).

37. The development of a range of social care and health care responses for drug misusers in Glasgow, supported by inter-agency co-operation and planning should have an impact over time in reducing the high number of drug-related deaths in the city. The setting up of the multi-disciplinary Glasgow Drug Problem Service is particularly welcome (para 5.4).

38. The Scottish Drugs Forum has been commissioned, through The Scottish Office, to develop information/publicity materials focusing on and directed at polydrug using injectors, highlighting these dangerous practices and providing commonsense advice on reducing the risks (para 5.5). All the agencies involved should take steps to ensure that in their contacts with persistent drug misusers they

continually emphasise the dangers of reckless injecting behaviour and polydrug misuse (para 5.6).

FUNDING

39. The Scottish Office should assess the usefulness of the information already provided by local authorities, and assess what additional information may be required on an annual basis, to provide a full picture of local authority expenditure on drug misuse services in Scotland (para 6.7).

40. Earmarked funding to health boards for the provision of services for drug misusers - that is both drug services programmes and the drugs element of HIV/AIDS programmes - should continue for the foreseeable future (para 6.8).

41. The Scottish Office should explore the possibility of setting an indicative spending level for local authority drug misuse services within grant-aided expenditure (para 6.9). If this proves possible, The Scottish Office should consider the scope for transferring the funding of voluntary sector projects with a strong social care element from health boards to social work departments (para 6.10).

42. As far as possible, contracts with the non-statutory sector to provide drug misuse services should be drawn up to cover reasonable periods of time (say 3 to 4 years) to provide conditions of financial stability within which services can be developed (para 6.11).

43. All applications for the funding of drugs-related projects under the Urban Programme should require to be endorsed by the area Drug Action Team. DATs should play a proactive part in developing such proposals (para 6.12).

CO-ORDINATION

44. In each health board area, a small group of senior people should be established to draw up an action plan for tackling drug misuse locally and thereafter driving and monitoring its delivery. This group - which should be known as the Drug Action Team - should consist of senior

local figures from the statutory and non-statutory agencies, including the health board, the social work department, the education department, the police and the voluntary sector (para 7.4).

45. The Drug Action Team should consist of officers who are at, or just below, chief officer level. The Chairman should be of chief officer level - that is to say a Health Board General Manager, a Social Work Services Director, a Director of Education, a Chief Constable or a person of similar standing. He or she should be selected through the machinery which exists locally for consultation at chief officer level, following whatever wider consultation seems appropriate. The Chairman should report regularly to the local chief officer's group on the activities of the Drug Action Team (para 7.6).

46. Drug Action Teams should be established in all health board areas by 1 April 1995. Within 6 months they should draw up strategic plans for tackling drug misuse in their areas. Although teams are to be locally based and not subject to central direction, The Scottish Office should monitor their development, should receive and assess their strategic and annual operating plans and should use its good offices to resolve any difficulties which arise locally (para 7.8).

47. The Scottish Office should provide funding to enable each Drug Action Team to have a Drugs Development Officer (para 7.10).

48. To support and inform the work of each Drug Action Team, a Drugs Forum, covering the same catchment area, should be established. This should be broadly based, representing the interests of those who provide services to drug misusers, drug misusers themselves and their families and carers and representatives of communities affected by drug misuse. The main purpose of the Forum would be to ascertain, co-ordinate and express the views of service providers, service users and those in need of services (para 7.11).

49. The Scottish Office should establish a Scottish advisory committee on drug misuse, reporting to the Secretary of State for Scotland, to provide advice on policy, priorities and strategic planning (para 7.14).

50. The development of a strategy for the training of those working in the drug misuse field should be taken forward by the Scottish advisory committee (para 7.17).

CRIMINAL JUSTICE ASPECTS

51. A study should be conducted of the impact of the introduction of the Glasgow Drug Problem Service on the criminal behaviour of drug misusers (para 8.6).

52. Decisions on diversion from prosecution should be made on the basis of the circumstances of the individual drug misuser and the alleged offence, as well as the substance concerned. The Lord Advocate should consider this approach in any guidance he issues to Procurators Fiscal in connection with diversion (para 8.12).

53. Sufficient provision for alleged offenders with drug related problems should be included in the proposed pilot social work diversion schemes to enable future policy and funding decisions to be made in the light of practical experience (para 8.14).

54. In consultation with Procurators Fiscal, Drug Action Teams should address the development of diversion schemes in their area within the context of their strategic plans (para 8.16).

55. There is scope for the greater use, especially in more rural areas, of programmes linked to probation supervision which can be used by the courts instead of custody. Local authorities should consider how this can be taken forward in the context of their 3 year strategic plans for offender services and the annual updates. Drug agencies should consider how they can provide a service linked to criminal justice disposals, which involve a measure of compulsion, and which require enforcement for non-compliance, alongside services provided on a voluntary basis (para 8.20).

56. There is a small group of vulnerable young offenders in the 16-18 age group who, in addition to the offences which have brought them to the attention of the authorities may also be experimenting with illicit drugs. However, prosecution of these young people might not be appropriate because of their immaturity. Local Authorities should therefore examine how best use may be made of resources and what programmes may need to be developed to enable these young offenders to be dealt with by the Children's Hearings (para 8.22).

57. Local authorities and health boards should examine the scope for incorporating substitute prescribing in programmes for drug misusing offenders linked to probation and other appropriate disposals (para 8.23).

58. Most drug misusers who are dealt with in the criminal justice system are likely to need combinations of similar health and social care services whether being dealt with in the context of prosecution, sentencing or release from custody. The Scottish Office should explore the feasibility of a single entry system to assessment for, and access to community social and health care services for drug misusers which might be used to assist decision-making at each stage in the criminal justice process (para 8.24).

PRISONS

59. The Scottish Prison Service should further develop reduction to abstinence and education programmes for long-term prisoners appropriate to the needs of the individuals (para 8.29).

60. The Medical Adviser to the Scottish Prison Service should make arrangements for all prison medical staff to have regular training sessions on drug misuse issues, either in-house or by attendance at external courses (para 8.31).

61. The Social Work Services Group of The Scottish Office and the Scottish Prison Service should consider the feasibility of a throughcare pilot scheme to determine what combination of support and advice for prisoners with drug problems (and their families), during imprisonment and following return to the community, might help the prisoner to remain drug free on release and assist the development of good practice (para 8.34).

62. Drug Action Teams should encourage arrangements to develop liaison between prisons in their area and community-based drug services on the lines developed in Tayside. It may be necessary to co-ordinate and support these local initiatives. SWSG and the Scottish Prison Service should consider how best this can be taken forward (para 8.35).

1 INTRODUCTION

1.1 Drug misuse is widely recognised as one of the most serious problems facing the United Kingdom and indeed many other countries across the world. During the last decade action, both domestically and internationally, has been taken against drugs on a massive scale, but the problem continues to grow. In Scotland all the available evidence points to drug misuse having increased substantially in the last 10 years. As with any illegal activity, precise information on the scale of the problem is difficult to obtain. However, the broad indicators which are available to measure prevalence such as information from the Scottish Drugs Misuse Database, from drug seizures by the police and HM Customs, from the number of recorded drugs offences and from the number of new drug addicts registered, all point to a sharp increase.

1.2 Drug misuse produces many problems for the individual misuser. Those who resort to injecting run risks of abscesses, septicaemia, gangrene and, where injecting equipment is shared, the risks that infected blood can transmit HIV and hepatitis. As has been tragically demonstrated in Glasgow and elsewhere, the dangerous practice of injecting can end in the ultimate price of the misuser losing his or her life. Dependent drug misusers may also be damaged in other ways; increasingly cut off from ordinary life, moving in a small circle of drug-orientated acquaintances, lacking or losing employment, becoming homeless or having insecure housing, and often turning to other crime or prostitution to finance their drug purchases. All of this can have a devastating effect on the families and friends of the individual misuser leading to the breakup of relationships and the breakdown of family life.

1.3 More generally the effects are also felt on society as a whole which has to bear the financial burden, such as the costs of drug-related crime, of enforcement and deterrence, and of medical and social care support for drug misusers and their families. The association of drugs with crime is three-fold; the misuse of drugs is itself a criminal offence, it gives rise to acquisitive crime as a means of obtaining money to purchase drugs and it sustains (and is sustained by) a criminal network of dealing and associated violence. The pervasive nature of drug misuse can also affect whole communities including those within them who have no personal or family involvement in drug misuse. Drug misuse tends to flourish in conditions of deprivation, alienation and poverty of aspiration. It is particularly prevalent in some of the peripheral housing schemes in Scotland's cities. It should be recognised, however, that it is also a growing problem in rural areas like the Borders and the Highlands.

1.4 While dependent drug misusers will often seek help for their addiction, there is deepening concern about the increasing use by young people of other drugs such as MDMA (Ecstasy), frequently associated with the "rave" dance scene, which has been linked with some recent deaths. The misuse of these drugs presents a particular dilemma in determining an effective response because, notwithstanding the potentially fatal consequences, the young people who take them do not, in the main, consider that they have a problem which needs help. The same can also be said for the most used of all the illegal drugs - cannabis, which accounts for some 80% of all recorded drugs offences. **The challenge for society - not just for the statutory and voluntary agencies charged with responding to the drug problem - is to reverse the cultural climate in which drug misuse thrives or, worse still, is accepted as the norm.**

1.5 Failure to respond effectively would carry a high price. If drug misuse were left unchecked it would have widespread and unacceptable consequences - corrupting young people, alienating families, bringing fear and disruption to communities, undermining public health and overburdening our services. Drug misuse has, therefore, to be recognised as a social problem which requires to be addressed as a national and local priority through measures to achieve personal, communal and cultural change.

1.6 While much valuable work has been carried out over many years by the various statutory and voluntary agencies operating in the drug misuse field there is a clear need to ensure that the present arrangements are relevant to current circumstances; are responsive to emerging needs; and are effectively co-ordinated in both planning and delivery. The requirement is to determine what further measures need to be taken in Scotland to strengthen action to prevent drug misuse and to ensure that services and initiatives at national and local level are provided and co-ordinated to optimum advantage.

1.7   To meet this challenge the Rt Hon Ian Lang MP, Secretary of State for Scotland, announced in April 1993 his decision to set up a Drugs Task Force under the chairmanship of Lord Fraser, Minister of State at The Scottish Office. The membership of the Drugs Task Force was drawn from the education, social work, health, police, voluntary sector and other relevant fields. Its terms of reference were as follows:-

"In the light of existing and emerging trends in drug misuse in Scotland:

-    to review current arrangements to prevent drug misuse and for the provision of services for misusers;

-    to consider what further practical measures might be taken; and

-    to assess the effectiveness of the present arrangements for co-ordination of action at national and local level."

The Drugs Task Force had its first meeting in September 1993 and subsequently met on a further 7 occasions.

1.8   To help fulfil its remit, the Drugs Task Force assembled a comprehensive picture of current drug misuse trends across Scotland and of the measures being taken in response. It collected information from the Health Education Board for Scotland, the Scottish Drugs Forum, the Association of Chief Police Officers In Scotland, the Glasgow Association of Family Support Groups and others including health boards, local authority education and social work departments, universities and further education colleges, and from the Chairmen of Drug Liaison Committees. In addition, submissions were also received from CREW 2000 and the Drugs Training Project, Stirling University. Information held centrally about the activities of other voluntary and independent bodies active in the drug misuse field was augmented by the personal knowledge of Drugs Task Force members. The subject areas reviewed as part of this information collecting exercise included:–

a. the scale and nature of the drug misuse problem in each area;

b. the prevention measures being taken in each area, including targeting and delivery;

c. the range of services provided for drug misusers in the area including counselling and advice, needle and syringe exchanges, detoxification facilities, rehabilitation facilities and substitute prescribing arrangements;

d. community care services for drug misusers and their families;

e. strategic planning;

f. liaison/involvement with the voluntary sector;

g. arrangements for co-ordination of local activity.

Views were also sought on what further practical measures might be taken to tackle drug misuse and to improve the current arrangements for co-ordination of action at national and local levels.

1.9　The Drugs Task Force is grateful to all the bodies concerned for the comprehensive written submissions which they provided. The wide range of issues covered enabled the Drugs Task Force to build up a picture of the action being taken around the country in tackling the drug misuse problem and was invaluable in informing our deliberations. From information available centrally, consideration was given to the issues surrounding drug misuse within prisons. The Drugs Task Force also had access to the excellent reports produced by the Advisory Council on the Misuse of Drugs (ACMD) on "AIDS and Drug Misuse Update" and on "Drug Education in Schools: The Need for New Impetus"; the report by Her Majesty's Inspectorate of Constabulary on how police forces in Scotland are tackling policing issues surrounding the misuse of drugs; and, towards the end of our deliberations, the report of the Scottish Affairs Committee into drug abuse in Scotland.

1.10　From the outset, the Drugs Task Force recognised that drug misuse is an enormously complex problem; that it is not a static situation but rather one in which new trends emerge and different dimensions appear; that neither the Government nor anyone else has a monopoly of wisdom on the subject and that no single agency, discipline or philosophy can combat drug misuse by itself. What was clear was the importance of a concerted and co-ordinated multi-agency approach which addressed the whole spectrum of drug misuse in Scotland embracing prevention, the criminal justice response, the provision of services, rehabilitation and aftercare in a co-operative way.

1.11 It cannot be denied that the response to the drug misuse problem in Scotland has developed in an ad hoc manner as the agencies have grappled with a constantly evolving and escalating problem. But it is also clear that a tremendous amount of energy and considerable resources have been put into tackling the effects of drug misuse. The Government funds a range of services whose programmes or a proportion of them are directed towards combating drug misuse. An estimated £42m was spent in tackling drug misuse in Scotland in 1992-93. The Drugs Task Force is encouraged by the considerable work presently being carried out by all the agencies concerned in responding to the problem; this provides an important base on which to build future effort. While strategic planning and co-ordination are critical factors in improving the response to drug misuse, it will be crucial, in developing the planning process, not to lose sight of the individual for whom all these efforts are directed and to harness the energy which the Task Force firmly believes to exist in many communities at local level in order to reverse the trend of drug misuse.

2 PREVALENCE AND DRUG MISUSE TRENDS

2.1   As in other countries, drug misuse in Scotland is not a unitary phenomenon. The types of drug used, the methods of administration, the regularity of use, the circumstances of use, the impact on a person's life and the degree of chemical dependence all vary widely. There is a spectrum of misuse from, at one end, the casual and occasional user of cannabis or one of the other so called "recreational" drugs in specific social situations to, at the other end, the regular and dependent injector of heroin or one of the other so called "hard" drugs, whose drug misuse dominates his or her whole life, and may indeed lead to his or her death.

2.2   What is distinctive about drug misuse in Scotland is the high level of injecting. On the basis of work conducted in Glasgow and Edinburgh a few years ago it has been estimated that there are some 20,000 regular or occasional injectors in Scotland. This is equivalent to a rate of 392 per 100,000 population. The estimate for the rest of the United Kingdom is 173 per 100,000. The high level of injecting is particularly significant because of the health risks attached to this form of drug misuse. The association in Scotland between intravenous drug misuse and the spread of HIV/AIDS is particularly strong. Moreover injecting can lead to death in other ways than through HIV/AIDS. Between November 1991 and January 1993, 73 injectors died suddenly in Glasgow as a direct result of their drug misuse. We discuss these deaths more fully in Chapter 5.

2.3   We know, or can reasonably infer, further details about the profile of injectors from the information supplied to the Scottish Drug Misuse Database and from research studies. Men outnumber women in the proportion of 5 to 2. The vast majority are less than 30 years of age. Many use a range of drugs - the so called polydrug users. From

7

information collected from services it appears that most injectors begin injecting in their middle teens, following a relatively brief period using drugs orally. Because of the health and social problems to which injecting gives rise, injectors are more likely to come to the attention of services. Of the 3685 new patients reported to the Scottish Drug Misuse Database in 1993, 52% had injected in the previous month, 17% had injected previously and 31% had never injected.

2.4 Even though injecting is such a serious problem in Scotland, injectors form only a minority of drug misusers. Unquestionably the drug most misused in Scotland is cannabis. In Scotland in 1992, 79% of police drug seizures were of cannabis and in 83% of cases of people found guilty of drugs offences, the drug was cannabis. In the 1993 Scottish Crime Survey 14% of the population surveyed acknowledged using cannabis at some point in their lives - which by extrapolation suggests that some 400,000-500,000 Scots, between the ages of 12 and 59, have used cannabis on at least one occasion. For people aged 12-29 the proportion was 19%. Other drugs taken orally include amphetamines, temgesic, benzodiazepines and LSD (although the first 3 of these can be and are also injected). Some drugs - such as Ecstasy - have become fashionable among young people involved in the rave scene. A small study conducted in 1992 suggested that 21% of the young people interviewed had taken Ecstasy and a further 10% had been offered but had declined.

2.5 Another particular feature of drug misuse in Scotland is the high incidence of the non-medical use of prescribed drugs, in particular painkillers such as Temgesic and Diconal and tranquillisers (benzodiazepines) such as Temazepam and Diazepam. Temgesic was the most common drug of misuse in the prescribed category notified to the Scottish Drug Misuse Database in 1991-92 (and second only to heroin overall); over 80% of the cases notified involved injecting. In 1992-93 Temgesic had been overtaken by Temazepam as the most commonly misused of the prescribed drugs notified. There are particular problems associated with the misuse of Temazepam especially in its gel formulation. Injection of the gel, after heating, carries a high risk of severe tissue damage and has led to a number of limb amputations. Action to address the problem of the misuse of prescribed drugs has been taken in a number of health board areas through voluntary bans on the prescribing of Temgesic and Temazepam. The ACMD has also advised the Government that

Temazepam should be re-scheduled from schedule 4 to schedule 3 of the Misuse of Drugs Regulations 1985 thus placing a range of tighter controls on the prescribing and possession of the drug. The Government is presently considering the ACMD advice.

2.6 Just as the type of drug misused and the method of administration vary, so do the social circumstances of misusers. Drug misuse is not confined to any one section of the population and those involved come from all types of background. However, as in other countries, there is a particular problem of "hard" drug misuse in some of the peripheral housing schemes of the Scottish cities, where it can have a blighting effect on community life not only in terms of the effect on misusers and their families but also in terms of the criminality and violence associated with drug dealing.

2.7 Some research studies suggest that for many drug misusers, drug taking becomes an "alternative lifestyle", providing a focus for the day's activities and giving the sense of purpose which legitimate work or leisure activity would otherwise provide. This "alternative lifestyle" undoubtedly exists in many deprived areas and provides a sub-culture of activity centred on obtaining money for drugs and participating in social networks in which drug misuse is conducted. The Scottish Affairs Committee in its report (paragraph 8) comments on the link between drug misuse and deprivation but observes that this link may not be as straightforward as it first seems. The report concludes that deprivation may not lead inexorably to drugs but drug misuse is an enormous problem in many areas of multiple deprivation. The Drugs Task Force shares this view. Care, however, must be taken not to stigmatise particular areas or communities. The Drugs Task Force recognises that the vast majority of people who live in the peripheral housing schemes most often associated with endemic drug misuse are not drug misusers and wish to see drug misuse eradicated from their communities. Drug misuse is not confined to any one section of society or limited to specific areas or communities.

THE ADEQUACY OF INFORMATION SYSTEMS

2.8 As the preceding discussion illustrates, a good deal of information is available about drug misuse in Scotland, both as a result of the routine collection of statistics and as a result of special exercises. However, data are not as complete or as reliable as might be wished.

The criminal justice system statistics record only those who come to police notice (and therefore movements up or down will reflect changes in policing policy or police effectiveness as much as in population behaviour); the records of those in contact with services give only a partial view; and even the records, derived from the death certification process, of drug related deaths have been shown by special studies to be incomplete. We have reviewed the arrangements for collecting information about drug misuse in Scotland.

2.9 Information about prevalence - the extent of drug misuse in the population - is important because of its significance for the development of policy and the delivery of services. It is also particularly difficult to obtain. Nevertheless, we consider that more effort should be put into producing reliable estimates of the extent of drug misuse in Scotland. We note that the 1993 Scottish Crime Survey offers one indicator of the extent of the problem; although figures offered as a result of self-reporting must always be treated with a degree of caution, this information is valuable and we consider that the self-reporting survey route should be further explored. We were also glad to hear that, drawing on experience in Glasgow in estimating the injecting population, The Scottish Office has recently commissioned a research study which aims to draw up a recommended model for estimating the extent of drug misuse in an area. Potentially, this is a very important line of development which would provide health boards, social work services and others with a means of assessing needs, and thus providing a basis for services.

2.10 To aid the development of accurate prevalence estimates, information on the use of drug services should be recorded. This is hard information, and ought to be capable of being captured. The Scottish Drug Misuse Database - which was introduced in 1990 - provides a framework for collecting information, and we wish to emphasise the importance which we attach to the comprehensiveness and reliability of this database. The Database currently collects anonymous information on demographic and behavioural characteristics of new drug misusers coming to the attention of services. Efforts to achieve 100% coverage should continue. **Consideration should also be given to extending the Scottish Drug Misuse Database to include all agency contacts between drug misusers and drug misuse services rather than just the first contact - the current arrangement - while maintaining the anonymity of the information collected.**

2.11 Assessments for social work services are an important source of information about the prevalence of drug misuse amongst those in contact with social work services and amongst members of their families. Social work authorities already collect such information as part of the referral arrangements for access to a number of social work services; for example, in community care assessments, social enquiry reports and assessments for reception of children into care. However, there may be scope for increasing the accuracy of this information and making it more accessible. **We recommend that social work authorities should review their arrangements for recording the incidence of drug misuse at the point of referral for social work services in order to ensure that those responsible for assessment across the full range of social work services are alert to the possibility that drug misuse may be a contributing factor, and that comprehensive information about prevalence is collected and made available to assist local service planning and the development of national policy objectives and priorities. Social workers who come into contact with drug misusers should be encouraged to make returns to the Scottish Drug Misuse Database, on Form SMR23.** Social work authorities might also consider the benefits of periodic audits of case records to check whether information about the incidence of drug misuse is being accurately recorded, to identify more precisely the volume and nature of referrals linked to substance misuse, and to assess the appropriateness of the services provided.

2.12 More broadly our consideration of the collection of information about drug misuse leads us to the conclusion that there is certainly scope for improvements to be made. On the other hand, we think it needs to be stated frankly that information about the extent of drug misuse is never likely to be as comprehensive and reliable as would ideally be wished. Nor should information be collected for its own sake, or for purely academic purposes. **Progress can best be made by a continuous process of seeking to improve the availability of reliable information, concentrating on what is required for policy development or the delivery of services. This needs to be taken forward positively at national level. We see this as one of the roles of the new Scottish advisory committee which we propose in Chapter 7.**

2.13 Overall prevalence figures are important, but for effective policy development and service planning they need to be combined with detailed needs assessment data. Needs assessment involves looking in detail at a representative sample of the drug misusing population, to ascertain social and health care needs. Only if this is undertaken, can service planning and policy development be conducted in a meaningful way. It will be essential therefore for health boards and social work departments to work together to develop effective systems for undertaking overall needs assessments of the drug misusing population (see the recommendation in Chapter 4.4).

3 PREVENTION

3.1 Prevention is better than cure. The Drugs Task Force's remit invited us to review the current arrangements to prevent drug misuse and to consider what further practical measures might be taken. It is our strong view that, while enforcement efforts need to be kept up, much more emphasis than hitherto should be given to measures to reduce the demand for drugs. This will require vigour, imagination and commitment. We have a number of proposals for taking this forward.

3.2 We wish to emphasise 2 fundamental points at the outset. First, the problem of drug misuse, and therefore its prevention, belong to the community as a whole. Drug prevention is often viewed as someone else's responsibility, when in fact everyone should be concerned and have a part to play. Second, no single prevention measure or activity - be it a mass media campaign, the work of the Health Education Board for Scotland, drugs education in schools, the prevention work undertaken by the police, health boards, social work departments and other agencies - can be viewed in isolation or as more important than another. There should be no expectation that a dose of education, information or publicity will solve the drug problem. What is required is a cohesive and targeted programme of action co-ordinated both at national and local level. In this chapter, we review the current arrangements for seeking to prevent drug misuse and propose improvements.

ACTION AT NATIONAL LEVEL

3.3 The Advisory Council on the Misuse of Drugs, in a 1984 report, defined drug prevention as "reducing the risk of an individual engaging in drug misuse and reducing the harm associated with drug misuse". One of its main conclusions was that there was a need for more effective, broadly-based programmes with the positive aim of promoting healthier lifestyles and which would include information about drugs and their effects. At GB-wide level this has been taken forward through a series of national mass media campaigns. These campaigns have been led by the Department of Health but The Scottish Office Home and Health Department has contributed both in terms of planning and in meeting the associated costs. Within the overall strategy, specific messages for the campaigns such as "Smack Isn't Worth It", "Don't Inject AIDS", "Drugs - The Effects Can Last Forever" have been adapted in the light of ongoing tracking and market research studies. In 1993-94 a national television advertising campaign was developed, directed at parents, with the aim of improving the quality of parents' conversation with their children on drug and solvent abuse. Two television commercials - one on drugs and one on solvents - highlighted the crucial role which parents should play in prevention. The key message was "If you don't talk to your child about drugs, someone else will". The campaign was backed up by a booklet specifically written and designed for parents of children aged 8-16 and aimed to make clear to parents that they have a vital role in preventing their child from using drugs and solvents and that they can influence their child's behaviour by discussing the issues with them in a balanced and informed way. In 1994-95 the national focus is being built around European Drug Prevention Week (15-22 October 1994) and like the successful EDPW in 1992 when the UK had the Presidency of the European Council, there will be an integrated campaign of drug prevention events and activities at GB level, throughout Scotland and at local community level.

3.4 The Scottish Affairs Committee in its report (paragraph 134) questioned the value of mass media campaigns in any form and suggests that they have "little to commend them". We have noted the Committee's reservations. Such campaigns are clearly not the whole remedy but, in our view, they have an important part to play in raising public awareness of drugs issues. Frequently in this report we refer to the pervasive and insidious nature of drug misuse. Its destructive consequences have been seen, time and again, across the whole social spectrum. Constant vigilance is therefore required to ensure that the threat of drug misuse is maintained in the general public consciousness and that its signs are readily recognised. We are in no doubt that mass media campaigns, skilfully presented, have the capacity to keep drug misuse in the public eye, to heighten awareness of its dangers and to reach large groups of people, for example, parents, who might otherwise choose to distance themselves from the issue. But to be effective such campaigns must be an integral, readily identifiable part of a concerted effort, with clearly defined objectives. Above all they must be - and be seen to be - relevant to the situation in Scotland. It will be crucial, therefore, at the early planning stages of prospective GB-wide campaigns to consider the relevance of a given proposed topic to the scene in Scotland and how it would complement other Scottish initiatives. Where these criteria are not satisfied, the scope for a separate Scottish campaign would fall to be considered. **We accordingly recommend that The Scottish Office should continue to support, and participate in mass media campaigns at GB level, providing that they are relevant to Scottish circumstances.**

3.5   We wish, however, to emphasise in relation to all mass media activity - whether carried out throughout Great Britain or only in Scotland - that evaluation is crucial. Already campaigns are subject to pre- and post-implementation evaluation; but increased attention should be given to developing and refining evaluation techniques so that reliable and informative assessment can be made of the impact of mass media interventions, thus allowing any lessons learned to be applied to subsequent campaigns.

3.6   The activities of the Health Education Board for Scotland (HEBS) in relation to drug misuse are aimed at raising awareness of the harm arising from drug misuse and the benefits of not misusing drugs; fostering motivation, attitudes, skills and behaviour which protect against drug misuse; promoting productive and healthful alternatives to drug misuse; and reducing the harm arising from drug misuse. HEBS deals with the topic of drug misuse in its general public programme, in its programmes centred on specific settings and sectors (most notably the community, schools and voluntary sector programmes), and through special projects. A key feature of the approach is that drug misuse is not handled in isolation, not least in view of the possible overlaps in causation of drug misuse, smoking and alcohol misuse and the links with other priority topics, such as HIV/AIDS. The HEBS programmes enable work on drug misuse to be incorporated into the wider approach of promoting lifeskills. They also provide materials and support for activities at more local levels, thus promoting co-ordination of health promotion effort in Scotland, and facilitate education for a range of 'health promoters'.

3.7   HEBS has conducted high profile campaigns targeting 14-17 year olds who are not using drugs or may be experimenting with drugs. These campaigns have been aimed at re-inforcing the ideas of being independent and being in control. Evaluation has confirmed a high level of awareness by the target group of the messages delivered by these campaigns and attraction to the materials used. Among its current activities the Board is developing and supporting drug education projects for young people, youth and community workers, parents and teachers; has a pilot project underway to assess the potential for distributing information on drugs, HIV/AIDS, etc at music concerts; has work ongoing within the concept of the health promoting school; and is involved in analysing the value of peer-led education. HEBS works in collaboration with health boards and national partners (including The Scottish Office, and national voluntary organisations).

3.8   The Drugs Task Force recognises the complexity and difficulty of drug prevention work with young people against the background in which they live their lives, taking account of peer pressure, socio-economic circumstances, the "fashionability" of certain drugs and other factors. The Scottish Affairs Committee in its report (paragraphs 133 and 134) acknowledges the merits of the lifeskills approach as regards drugs prevention work but it questions whether even this has a significant effect in deterring drug misuse. The Drugs Task Force believes that HEBS should continue its commitment to the lifeskills/healthy lifestyles approach. **It has an important leadership role at the cutting edge of prevention work and should actively seek out innovative approaches in its work on drug misuse.** We particularly welcome the Board's commitment to ensuring that its activities are based on relevant research at the planning stage, appraisal at the developmental stage and evaluation after implementation. We recognise the value of the HEBS Scotland-wide population based approach and we consider that there is a need for further targeted approaches. A potentially fruitful avenue of exploration might be to focus preventive activity on particularly vulnerable groups of young people eg in peripheral housing schemes. Clearly careful research would need to be carried out to determine how such prevention work might be developed for the target groups. **We recommend that priority should be given to the development of preventive work targeted on groups of young people who** because of their environment or other factors are particularly vulnerable to drug misuse pressures. HEBS and The Scottish Office should determine how this is to be taken forward, if necessary deflecting resources from The Scottish Office's drugs publicity budget.

HARM MINIMISATION

3.9   In developing their drug prevention strategies, HEBS and the other agencies also have to address the issue of harm minimisation. A difficult balance has to be struck between the ultimate goal of a society free from drug misuse and the more pragmatic objective of minimising the harm, both for the individual and for society as a whole, which flows from drug misuse. Viewed from one perspective the provision of needle exchange arrangements can be seen as condoning illegal drug misuse. Viewed from another it can be seen as a sensible and pragmatic step in damage limitation. The concept of harm minimisation has given rise to much philosophical debate. Our view is that each case has to be judged on its merits. Some forms of harm minimisation - such as needle exchanges and substitute prescribing - are here to stay. But these are rightly subject to restrictions. In appropriate circumstances it seems to us that harm minimisation has an important part to play in the prevention and education effort. For example it seems to us right that health education campaigns should explain, in appropriate terms, how needles can best be sterilised or how those attending "raves" can minimise the risks of Ecstasy use, through drinking soft drinks and "chilling out". We believe, therefore, that in the prevention and education fields, harm minimisation is a legitimate approach. This is not to condone drug taking but simply to acknowledge that it would be foolish to pretend that drug taking of this kind does not take place; and therefore the pragmatic response is to provide information and advice about minimising the risks. However, in applying the harm minimisation approach, the risks involved in drug misuse should never be under-played and the message that abstinence is the only risk-free option must be emphasised.

ACTION AT LOCAL LEVEL

3.10   Health boards, local authority community education departments, social work departments, the police, voluntary agencies and others are all active at local level in delivering the prevention message and backing it up in appropriate ways. From the information provided to the Drugs Task Force there emerges an encouraging picture of co-operation between the various agencies but there is a need to ensure that co-ordination is effective, that the message being delivered is consistent and that targeting of the most vulnerable groups is done to the best effect. In addition, an active and interested local media can be of great help and support, both to promote consideration of issues and to assist measured and well-informed local strategies to prevent drug misuse, and to increase access to services. It is in the interests of local communities, and those who plan and deliver services to work constructively with the local media, to create a well-informed environment and to stimulate consideration of measures which may help in countering the phenomenon of drug use, which creates considerable concern and anxiety for communities throughout Scotland.

HEALTH BOARDS

3.11 Health boards have a responsibility for assessing the health status of their population; setting priorities and targets; and ensuring that their local population receives appropriate health promotion programmes. A major recent development has been the setting up of health liaison groups or health alliances at local level. The prevention of drug misuse is an important part of health boards' health promotion programmes and features prominently in the work of health promotion departments. Amongst a wide range of activity undertaken by health boards is the distribution of publicity material (posters and leaflets), teaching packs, videos, etc about the dangers of drug misuse. Health boards are also very active in initiating, supporting and organising conferences, open-days and teach-ins about the issues surrounding drug misuse. There is also encouraging evidence of good co-operation between health boards and education authorities in presenting programmes in the school setting. Health boards clearly recognise the importance of their responsibilities for health promotion and a number have appointed health promotion officers who have a specific responsibility for action on drug prevention often in association with other prevention responsibilities such as for HIV/AIDS.

3.12 The Drugs Task Force believes that health boards with their wide-ranging responsibilities for health promotion and services and their influence on health professionals who are in the front line of action against drugs have an important and pivotal role to play in drugs prevention work. However, we share the concern of the Scottish Affairs Committee that health boards' activities in this area should be subject to careful evaluation since there is clearly little point in continuing with an approach if there is no evidence that it is successful. **The importance of ensuring that drug prevention work is developed along clear strategic lines with identifiable aims and objectives, a focused approach on delivery to its target audience and built in evaluation of its outcome must be emphasised.** The need to develop strategies to prevent drug misuse (and for the provision of services for misusers) has been identified in the Priorities and Planning Guidance issued by the NHS Chief Executive to health boards in December 1993. The NHS Management Executive in Scotland will be monitoring progress by boards.

COMMUNITY EDUCATION

3.13　The role of community education is an expanding one and the information provided to the Drugs Task Force reveals a considerable degree of effort being expended by the community education service and others. A range of activities and initiatives has been developed encompassing advice and information, counselling young people at risk, etc in tackling the issues of drugs and HIV/AIDS. In a number of areas particular initiatives are being pursued. These include a project in Lothian to contact "hard to reach" groups of young people who do not attend formal institutions such as schools and youth centres. In Tayside the Health Board and the Regional Council's Education Department jointly fund a post within the Community Education Service with responsibility for promoting health issues specifically in connection with drugs and HIV/AIDS. A diversity of approach in the community education field is undoubtedly the way forward. As we have recommended in other chapters of this report, evaluation must be a key element in the development of this preventive work.

SOCIAL WORK

3.14　At present, social work departments' main role in prevention is in promoting harm reduction strategies and providing a range of services for drug misusers and their families. The Drugs Task Force recognises that social work department staff are also well placed to play an important role in prevention activities, through their work with children and families. It is recognised that children from socially disadvantaged and dysfunctional families are far more likely to come into contact with the drug culture, to be drawn into drug misuse and experience its harmful consequences. Social workers caring for these families are well placed not only to convey prevention messages but also to help parents acquire the skills they need to help their children avoid experimentation or reduce the risk of them being further drawn into the drug scene if they have already begun to experiment. Information via national and local prevention initiatives must be backed up in this way through improved local service networks so that parents have the practical assistance they need, at the right time, to help their children. A significant element of work with young people in this area is carried out by the voluntary sector child care organisations who have demonstrated their alertness to embracing drug-related issues. For all of this work to be effective, it must be co-ordinated with health and education initiatives at both national and local level. **We recommend that local authority social work departments and the voluntary sector child care organisations should incorporate drugs prevention activity in their work with children and young people. Furthermore their efforts in this direction should be co-ordinated with local and national health and education initiatives.**

CO-ORDINATION

3.15 This plethora of activity in the prevention field is encouraging but, while there is strength in diversity, there is also a need for a coherent, structured approach. Good co-ordination of the drug prevention work of all the agencies involved - to ensure consistency and effectiveness of effort and delivery - is therefore vitally important if the maximum impact is to be achieved. HEBS has an important role in developing and implementing national initiatives and in providing support and materials for more locally based activities. But we believe that, in addition, there is a need for a strategic overview to be taken. **We consider that this high level co-ordination of policy on drugs prevention at national level should be carried out by the new Scottish advisory committee which we propose should be set up (see Chapter 7); and we so recommend. At local level Drug Action Teams (see Chapter 7) should develop a prevention** strategy for their area which is consistent with national policy and aimed at complementing and building on the work undertaken by HEBS and local agencies. DATs would plan, develop and operate their strategy through their constituent local agencies - social work departments, health boards, education departments, the police, voluntary sector bodies etc.

PEER LED EDUCATION

3.16 The term "peer education" describes the process whereby young people receive information and learn skills from other young people aimed, in the health and social education field, at enabling them to improve and safeguard their own health. While this has been a well developed and widely used approach to promoting the health of young people in countries such as Australia, Holland, and the USA (where it has been developing since the late 70s) it is a relatively recent innovation in this country. There is no doubt that young people view their peers as an important source of information, guidance and practical support on many aspects of life during the process of growing up.

3.17 A number of peer led education projects are underway in Scotland including a pilot project in Ayrshire involving 15 young people in the 14-20 age group who have been recruited for an intensive training programme. Evolving from their training the peer educators developed a drug education programme aimed at their peers in youth clubs, schools and other community settings. In the Forth Valley area a peer led drug education project entitled "Wisecrack" is underway with the aim of preventing persistent drug use and promoting positive lifestyles. The focus of this programme is on young people's views and attitudes to drugs and involves a group of trained volunteers (aged 16-25 years) working with young people (aged 13-17 years). A HEBS-supported collaborative peer education project is also underway in Fife based in two secondary schools and a further education college. The main aims of the project are to establish the needs of young people in relation to health education and service provision concerning sexual behaviour, HIV/AIDS and drugs and to enable young people to become effective educators of their own peer group. Another interesting project which has recently been established in Lothian with financial assistance from The Scottish Office is Crew 2000. Crew 2000 is a group of young "ravers"/club goers and drug workers who together have developed a peer information/education programme aimed at young people. The aim is to recruit young people, who are familiar with and educated about the recreational drug scene, as volunteers in order to develop a user-led, out-of-hours service to make contact with the youngsters, with a view to making them aware of the dangers of drug misuse and to promote healthy choices.

3.18 It is too soon to assess the outcome of these projects. Peer-led education appears to have the potential to enhance the ability of young people to provide each other with accurate information on health and other issues. It does so by using language and approaches understandable to young people and perhaps in ways more readily acceptable than the more conventional "teacher and taught" method. This approach may have particular potential in relation to those who may be experimenting or on the fringes of drug misuse. While the Drugs Task Force is keen that innovative approaches of this kind should be tried it is vital that the existing projects are fully evaluated before an unreserved endorsement can be given to this approach. The Drugs Task Force welcomes the innovative pilot work being undertaken in this field and looks forward to the outcome of the evaluation of the current projects. **We recommend that if the peer-led education approach proves successful it should be developed.**

DRUG EDUCATION IN SCHOOLS

3.19 Education about drugs is taught as one element of the health education which is offered in all Scottish schools, and the implementation of the 'health promoting school' concept by The Scottish Office Education Department and HEBS has provided a context for a wider focus on health issues, including drug misuse. The school curriculum in Scotland is not laid down by Parliament and responsibility lies with education authorities and with headteachers to decide the broad scope and detailed content of study programmes. In health education, as in other subjects, schools follow national guidelines. For pupils aged 5-14, there are guidelines on Environmental Studies and guidelines on Personal and Social Development. In primary schools, health education is taught by class teachers. In secondary schools, trained guidance teachers deliver most health education, typically as part of a personal and social education programme although some aspects are covered in science, home economics, technical education and physical education.

Outside speakers such as police officers and health experts are also used in both primary and secondary schools.

3.20   Within health education, a balance is sought between the promotion of good health in general, and the specific targeting of activities which put the health of young people at risk. The development of self confidence, mature relationships with others and the ability to assess risks and make independent choices are important. All of these have the capacity to help protect young people against the risks of addiction and abuse. Within this broad approach specific education about drugs, HIV/AIDS, smoking and alcohol misuse takes place and the consequences of hazardous behaviour are stressed - for example, the sharing of needles by young people to inject drugs which may lead to HIV infection.

3.21   A range of teaching materials is available to schools but the main teaching package on drugs education is "Drugwise Too" aimed at 10-14 year olds. This material was distributed to all Scottish schools at the end of 1992 and replaced the earlier "Drugwise" 12 to 14 package which schools have used since 1986. In addition HEBS produces materials for use by young people, school teachers and parents.

3.22   Demonstrating the effectiveness of drugs education in schools is extremely difficult. Drugs education in Scotland was extensively reviewed in 1989. The study found that drugs education was effective in providing young people with accurate information about the effects of drug use but there was no conclusive evidence about its influence on attitudes or practices. The evaluation results reinforced previous evidence that there is no simple relationship between knowledge, attitudes and behaviour, and this is not limited to drugs education or to schools in particular. However, the evidence does point to a skills based approach although the provision of clear and unambiguous information is also essential. Research studies carried out in various countries over the past 25 years into the range of prevention approaches used confirms that the "say no to drugs" and the "shock-horror" approaches are at best ineffective and at worst counter-productive. Programmes based around these approaches can mislead young people about the scale of risk involved and can encourage drug use among those young people who see it as a challenge or rebellion.

3.23   The Drugs Task Force has considered reports provided by Directors of Education in Scotland and the Report "Drugs Education in Schools: The Need for New Impetus" by the Advisory Council on the Misuse of Drugs (ACMD). As far as the scale and nature of the drug problem among schoolchildren in Scotland is concerned, there is no definitive information on prevalence since the 1989 study which showed that 20% of pupils in S2-S4 (aged about 13-16) reported experimentation with illegal drugs on at least one occasion. In their reports to the Task Force the Directors of Education for Grampian, Highland and Orkney all referred to local lifestyle surveys of prevalence among school age children. These surveys indicated that between 16% (Orkney) and 27% (Grampian) of adolescents had taken an illegal drug on at least one occasion; the Highland study revealed that cannabis and solvents were the most commonly misused substances although 1% of the survey group claimed to have tried heroin. More recently, the 1993 Scottish Crime Survey included a self-reporting questionnaire about drugs for a sample (500) of 12-15 year olds across Scotland. Unfortunately some 8% of the group failed to complete the drugs questions and this reduces the reliability of the results. However, among those aged 12 and 13 in the sample, 3% reported ever having misused a drug; 1% of 12-13 year olds reported having used cannabis, 1% LSD, 1% magic mushrooms, and less than half a percent Temazepam. None reported having used opiates. For those aged 14 and 15 the figures rise significantly; some 16% reported ever having misused drugs with 13% having used cannabis, 4% amphetamines, 4% LSD, 5% magic mushrooms, 3% Ecstasy, 3% Temazepam and less than 1% opiates. **We consider that there is undoubtedly a need for regular information on the prevalence of drug misuse among school age children in order to inform the planning and development of drug prevention measures in schools.**

3.24   Many factors influence children's behaviour and we should not have unreasonable expectations about the ability of schools to dissuade young people from drug misuse. Nevertheless schools have an important role to play in informing young people about the hazards involved and in seeking to ensure that as few as possible of the children under their guidance misuse drugs. Schools provide a key environment for the development of lifeskills to equip pupils to make informed decisions about the issues surrounding drug misuse and to take avoiding action. It is important that full opportunity is taken, both in primary and in secondary schools, to provide information, instruction and guidance on drug-related issues. Research by the Scottish Council for Research in Education published in June 1993 found that in its sample of 142 primary schools, 40% were providing drugs education to pupils in primary 6 and 7. In the sample of 128 secondary schools, over 90% covered drugs education at some stage (mainly in S3 and S4). The Drugs Task Force is aware that there is great pressure on the school curriculum. However, given the scale of the problem and the importance of ensuring that our young people are given information about drugs appropriate to their age in a consistent and reasoned way we believe that headteachers must be reminded of the importance of drugs education. **In this regard we share the view expressed in the Scottish Affairs Committee Report (paragraph 137) that an adequate amount of time must be devoted to drugs prevention activities within all primary and secondary schools.** While the Drugs Task Force recognises the practical difficulties for primary schools in finding time to implement drugs education for the younger age group this must nevertheless be addressed. We believe that focusing on the whole package of environment, science, health and other topics within which drugs education might be placed would help set the tone and provide a context for primary school pupils from an early age. Co-operation and liaison between primary and secondary schools in developing and delivering drugs prevention education is, we believe, essential. **We recommend that The Scottish Office Education Department should issue guidance for all schools in Scotland stressing the importance of drugs prevention education and the need to continue to emphasise this within the syllabus.**

3.25 **Within their responsibilities for school inspection work generally, Her Majesty's Inspectorate of Schools should have regard to how schools are tackling drug prevention education with a view to stimulating increased activity where this is shown to be necessary, disseminating good practice and ensuring that a consistent approach is taken throughout the country.**

3.26 The video and associated teaching package "Drugwise Too" for the 10-14 age group is widely used throughout Scotland. By focusing on the lifeskills approach, it provides what is generally acknowledged as the most suitable method of dealing with the issue of drug misuse for this age group. However, the reports from Directors of Education and the ACMD Report point to gaps in provision across the school age range. While some individual education authorities have taken initiatives in providing drugs prevention education for S5 and S6 pupils, there is no nationally approved package for senior pupils in Scottish schools. Nor is any drugs prevention work being undertaken for the under 10 age group. The ACMD Report expresses concern that many young children under 10 are exposed to the drugs scene and are often well aware of drug misuse at an early age but are not being provided with drug prevention education until much later in their school life. **We recommend the development by The Scottish Office Education Department of new drug prevention packages for use in primary schools, focusing on children in the under-10 age group, and on senior secondary pupils in the 15-18 age group.**

3.27 Who can best deliver drugs education in schools? As indicated above in primary schools this is the responsibility of the class teacher while in secondary schools, trained guidance teachers mainly deliver drugs education within the health education syllabus. In-service training on drugs misuse for teachers is provided through the wider health education training programme. It is carried out on a fairly uniform basis across the country but needs to be reviewed on a regular basis and geared to the materials being used by the schools. Drugs education training should be given to teachers, both when they are receiving their initial teacher training and during in-service training. Developing a national strategy for substance misuse training for all those groups whose work impacts on the drugs field (as well as teachers) is dealt with in Chapter 7. The role of outside speakers such as the police, health experts, drugs workers, and former drug users raises sensitive issues. The Drugs Task Force is concerned that, while outside speakers may be well motivated and have the best intentions, they may not be the most effective channel for delivering drug prevention messages and in some instances their involvement may be counterproductive. While the Drugs Task Force does not wish to dismiss out of hand the contribution that non-educationists might make in the drug prevention field, this needs careful thought and planning. **We recommend that the Scottish Office Education Department should issue policy guidance to ensure that a consistent approach is adopted regarding non-educationists who deliver drugs education in schools.**

3.28 Children are in school for only one-ninth of their lives between the ages of 5 and 16 years and there are limits to what we can expect schools to achieve in seeking to influence how young people use their free time out of school. Links between home and school can be helpful. Information to parents about what their children will be taught in this area of the curriculum, and why, may alert them to keep a closer eye on what their children are doing in their spare time. It is clear from media reports and from other sources that incidents of drug taking in or around schools or involving schoolchildren take place. It is important that schools should have a clear policy on how incidents involving the possession, selling or use of drugs by schoolchildren should be handled. The management of drug-related problems in schools is covered in the ACMD Report. ACMD suggests that schools' drugs policy needs to be consistent, to balance the interests of the pupils and the reputation of the school, to protect other pupils and to help those who do misuse drugs. It advocates a consistent policy which has been the subject of discussion by all those involved within the school, including parents. We believe that parents should therefore be brought into the policy making process. This process should cover both how schools handle drug-related incidents and, more generally, why and how drugs education issues are delivered in the school. This might best be achieved through school boards or parent/teacher associations which have the capacity to foster closer links between schools and parents. **We recommend that The Scottish Office Education Department should issue guidance to schools, school boards and parent/teacher associations on the development of a comprehensive drugs policy and what this should cover.**

CHILDREN IN CARE

3.29 Children taken into care by a local authority have the same day to day educational needs and face the same pressures as other children in respect of substance misuse. Consequently it is important to acknowledge the problem and strive to ensure that children in care and those who look after them are given every assistance. The statutory provisions covering children in care are contained in the Social Work (Scotland) Act 1968. Care can be provided by the local authority on a voluntary basis (when parents are temporarily unable to look after their own children) or on a compulsory basis normally following a decision of the Children's Hearing or the court. Care can either be provided in a home environment (eg with relatives or foster parents) or in a residential setting which might provide secure facilities. The number of children (under 16) in care in Scotland and away from home is around 4,500 with a little over half of these children placed in foster care and the remainder in residential care.

3.30 While there is no evidence to suggest that a disproportionate number of children in care have problems relating to substance misuse, when children in need of care and protection do experience problems, they are likely to be more serious. The report of the Chief Inspector of Social Work Services for Scotland "Another Kind of Home" in 1992 reviewed residential child care and stressed that children and young people in care should be made aware of the dangers to health caused by drugs, solvent and alcohol misuse. The report emphasised that children misusing drugs and other substances present particular problems for staff in residential establishments although it pointed out that care staff are uniquely placed to promote healthy lifestyles for those in their care and should do so in collaboration with local health education staff. The report recommended that local authorities which have not done so should prepare practice guidance for care staff on drug, alcohol and solvent misuse and appropriate information for young people in care.

3.31 The ACMD report on drug education in schools also deals with the question of drug education for children in care. Children in care require to be educated to the normal standards laid down within the Scottish education system. This may be achieved by children attending local schools in the normal way (for example where they are under supervision at home) or in residential schools where they can receive tuition "inhouse". Drug education materials made available through schools should also be available to children in care. In addition it is important for local authorities where they are "in loco parentis" to ensure that drug prevention education is supplemented as appropriate through further information, advice and support for the children in their care and parents or foster parents of children under supervision. For this to be effective local authorities will need to be aware of the prevalence of substance misuse amongst children in their care. **We recommend that local authorities should ensure that social workers preparing reports for Children's Hearings or supervising children in care are alert to the possibility that a child may be experimenting with drugs and other substances, and that the misuse of drugs and other substances is routinely monitored to ensure that children in care who have problems in this respect get the help they need at the earliest opportunity.**

3.32 The Drugs Task Force welcomes the initiative of the Social Work Services Group of The Scottish Office in grant aiding the Drugs Training Project at Stirling University and the Centre for Alcohol and Drug Studies at Paisley University for the purpose of developing training opportunities for residential care staff to increase their understanding and practice skills in working with young people who may be experimenting with alcohol, drugs and solvents. It is encouraging that the early signs suggest that this initiative has been welcomed by local authorities and the voluntary sector.

3.33   The White Paper "Scotland's Children" (Cm 2286) pointed out that when young people emerge from a period in care - whatever form it takes - they can go through an unsettling time: they may be particularly vulnerable and in need of support. They may well be exposed to the lure of drugs as a relief from personal pressures and uncertainties. The Government propose to strengthen the duties and powers of local authorities to advise and assist young people during a period in care and to assist young people after they have been in care. Help and advice to help prevent experimentation with drugs should be a constant feature of such aftercare.

THE FURTHER AND HIGHER EDUCATION SECTOR

3.34   The circumstances of higher education - young people away from home, under pressure to succeed and a vibrant social life - provide an environment in which experimentation with drugs can flourish. The Principals of universities and colleges in the Higher and Further Education sectors in Scotland were invited to submit reports to the Drugs Task Force on the scale and nature of the drug problem among students, drug prevention initiatives undertaken, training in drugs issues for staff and the existence of a drugs prevention strategy. An encouragingly large number of replies was received. None of the further and higher education institutions which responded have detailed information on prevalence although many acknowledge concern about the use of drugs by students and have information on specific incidents involving individual students who have come to the attention of the authorities for the misuse of drugs. While some colleges report incidents involving heroin, in the main the drugs involved are in the recreational category - cannabis, Ecstasy, LSD, etc. Drug prevention information is covered, in many instances, in the induction packs given to students on taking up their studies and we would commend this approach to all universities and colleges. A number of colleges publicise the drug prevention message through the use of posters and literature as well as arranging for talks to be given by the police. We welcome the health orientated approach adopted by many of the colleges in co-operation with health boards and other agencies. It is encouraging that so many of the responses appreciated the need for guidance/counselling staff, in particular, to have training in drugs education issues and for other staff to be aware of the problem; a number of colleges have taken steps to obtain the necessary training from recognised sources. However, few colleges appear to have a coherent drugs strategy although a number are addressing this omission. We believe that more attention needs to be given to drugs issues in higher education establishments. **We recommend that The Scottish Office should issue guidance to all further and higher education institutions in Scotland on the issues which should be covered in a drugs strategy for these bodies.**

THE POLICE

3.35 While the primary role of the police as far as drug misuse is concerned is to pursue those who traffic and deal in illegal drugs, investigate drug-related offences and enforce the law, the police also have an important role in demand reduction and prevention. Police forces in Scotland, mainly through their Community Involvement Branches, work within the community in promoting an awareness of drugs issues and through discussions, liaison and involvement with a range of community groups seek to have an impact on prevention strategies. Police activity in this area is extremely important and the Drugs Task Force welcomes the clear evidence of police commitment to the co-operative multi-agency approach to tackling drug misuse. The police also actively participate in drugs education in schools with officers from Community Involvement Branches and from Force Drugs Squads providing an input through the Drugwise programmes. Police officers also frequently talk to headteachers and senior staff about the drug misuse problems in their particular areas. The Drugs Task Force welcomes the high profile given by police forces in Scotland to drug prevention work and commends the recommendations contained in Her Majesty's Chief Inspector of Constabulary's Thematic Inspection Report published in December 1993. In particular we endorse the view expressed in the report that the drugs prevention message requires to be delivered in an effective and consistent way in schools. In this regard the police are no different from those other non-educationists who might be involved in delivering drugs education in schools (see paragraph 3.27). The principal role of the police in relation to drug prevention work in schools must be in support of the teachers whose responsibility it is for delivering the subject in class. However, where - with the agreement of the school - police officers are used directly in class work in support of the teacher, it will be important to ensure that these police officers are selected because of their communication abilities, and subsequently receive the relevant and necessary training to fulfil this role effectively. **We recommend that the Association of Chief Police Officers in Scotland and the Association of Directors of Education in Scotland should co-operate in developing training packages for police officers engaged in school liaison work.** We also share the view expressed in the other reports previously mentioned that regular evaluation of the police input to drugs education should be carried out. This might best be undertaken by education authorities in conjunction with police forces.

RESEARCH

3.36 A constantly recurring theme at Drugs Task Force meetings was the need for more information about what factors influence young people to misuse drugs. The more we know about why people misuse drugs, how they start down the route of misuse and how they can be helped, then the better informed we are in devising effective strategies for handling the problem. Research in this area is vital. It is crucial to have a sound basis for policy formulation, decision making, resource allocation and for the evaluation of policy and practice. There has been a considerable amount of research carried out into drug misuse internationally and Scotland has contributed to this activity. In Scotland important work has been done, especially in investigating the link between drugs, prostitution and HIV, and also in estimating the prevalence of drug injecting in the community. Research projects currently being carried out and funded by The Scottish Office include a study into the use of Ecstasy in Glasgow; an evaluation of harm reduction in prisons; and the use of probation orders for drug offenders. The Drugs Task Force welcomes the recent decision by the Chief Scientist Office of The Scottish Office to fund a programme of research covering three principal areas of study as follows:–

(a) Prevalence of persistent drug misuse. The basis of this study has been described in Chapter 2.

(b) Routes into drug misuse. Recognising the need for research into young people's vulnerability to drug misuse, the research here will aim to identify the early formation of perceptions, attitudes and experiences that might influence subsequent drug misuse or, more importantly, protect against such misuse. The research should identify information relating to the design and targeting of prevention strategies. It will involve interviewing young people and groups of parents from a range of backgrounds, and will consider differences in the vulnerability of the young to drug misuse across urban and rural settings as well as between areas which are relatively affluent or deprived.

(c) Routes out of drug misuse. Once established, drug misuse is a behaviour from which it is difficult to escape. The reasons for this are likely to be a combination of pharmacological addiction and attachment to particular lifestyles. Even so, some people are successful in modifying or ending drug misuse (in much the same way as some people "grow out of" crime). Accordingly, the proposal is to investigate those individuals who have been able to end or modify drug taking behaviour in order to identify the specific combination of factors that may have been influential. This will entail looking at the possible influence of life events, involvement with treatment agencies and changes in life circumstances. The study will consist of detailed interviews (a) with individuals who have successfully modified their drug misuse behaviour as a result of different strategies and (b) with a comparison group of individuals who had failed in their attempts to change their behaviour.

The Drugs Task Force commends the proposed research in these vital areas. The nature of drug misuse suggests the need for a continued series of studies covering a variety of drug misuse issues which will assist with the formulation of effective drug prevention strategies. **We can see a continuing need for research into drug misuse. We recommend that The Scottish Office should take steps to ensure that a suitable research programme is developed and sustained.**

THE DRUG PREVENTION INITIATIVE

3.37 The Scottish Affairs Committee in its Report recommends (paragraph 138) that consideration should be given to expanding the Drug Prevention Initiative in Scotland. The Drug Prevention Initiative (DPI) was first announced by the Home Office in October 1989 and was designed to promote drugs prevention in neighbourhoods most at risk from drugs misuse. The concept was that a conventional top-down campaign was likely to have only limited effect but that local communities, properly informed, encouraged and supported, could play a vital role in exerting pressure against drug misuse in whatever form it might take. The DPI sought the active participation of interested local people, professional, statutory and voluntary organisations to build on current local work in education and health and to seek to mobilise local communities to initiate, promote and sustain drug prevention activity. The idea was to create a diverse and innovative range of activities, such as media projects run by youth workers, peer education projects in schools and information campaigns. In Scotland projects were set up under the DPI in Dundee (in December 1991) and in Glasgow (in March 1992). An independent evaluation of the Drugs Prevention Initiative commissioned by the Home Office has confirmed the success of the concept and has recommended continuation but with more focus on establishing what works most effectively in the drug prevention arena. Locally-based action of the sort pioneered by the DPIs is vital and must be developed if drug misuse is to be successfully countered at local level.

COMMUNITY ACTION

3.38 It is our view that a major and often unexplored source of energy against drug misuse lies within the community and the Drugs Task Force believes that, given the right lead, community energy can be galvanised to tackle the drug problem within local areas. In particular there is a need to encourage and support community action to tackle drug misuse involving groups such as parents, churches, local schools and local business interests, as well as the statutory and voluntary agencies. In some cases the focus might be on activity-led initiatives developing young people's interests in games, crafts and other leisure pursuits which would steer them away from drug-related influences. We believe that this local energy might be channelled through the introduction of schemes at community level to initiate action against drug misuse. **We recommend that pilot community drug action schemes should be developed in a number of areas with a view to determining whether such initiatives could be applied successfully on a wider basis.**

CONCLUSION

3.39 In concluding this chapter, we wish to emphasise that drugs prevention and positive health promotion activity should be seen as a component in a range of work and relationships with young people. In addition to the formal educational provision in schools and community education, many youth organisations have opportunities of contact and involvement with young people, which can be effective in affecting lifestyle and attitudes. In addition, others who work professionally with young people, or who have responsibilities towards them, including GPs, youth leaders, and members of childrens panels, should consider how they can contribute further, both by ensuring that they are well informed on issues of drug misuse, and by using their contacts with young people to good effect in assisting them to avoid drug related harm.

4 THE PROVISION OF SERVICES

4.1   While efforts to prevent the misuse of drugs are of prime importance, it would be naive to presume that such misuse, which has been with us throughout history, is ever going to be totally eradicated. There will always be people who misuse drugs (and other substances). Given the social and health problems which ensue for those who become dependent on particular controlled drugs there will be a continuing need for a range of responsive health and social services. Drug misuse often commences in the early to mid-teens, peaking at 20-24 and declining in the late 20s and early 30s. If individual misusers can be kept in touch with services through this period they can reduce the harm they cause to themselves and others, lessen their involvement with drugs and, in many cases, return to a drug-free lifestyle earlier than might otherwise have been the case. **Consequently there is a need to treat each drug misuser as an individual and to have in place arrangements for treatment and social care which seek to enable the misuser to extricate himself or herself from drug misuse and all it entails.** It is also essential to monitor and evaluate how well these services match need and achieve their objectives, and how efficiently they use resources. In this chapter, we review the current arrangements for the provision of services and make recommendations for change and development.

RANGE OF SERVICES PROVIDED

4.2   The treatment and rehabilitation needs of drug misusers vary greatly. They may include treatment for acute medical crises (eg an overdose), advice and counselling, help in withdrawing from drugs, intervention in and resolution of acute social problems - such as 3.24

homelessness, unemployment, family breakdown, legal problems - and long term support during recovery. In the case of more serious physical complications arising from drug misuse, such as septicaemia or AIDS, treatment is provided within the range of general medical services, including - in crises - hospital accident and emergency services. The services required to respond to these demands are provided in the main by health boards, local authority social work and housing departments and the voluntary and private sectors. So far as health services are concerned, about 20 hospitals in Scotland provide facilities, including in-patient detoxification, out-patient clinics, day centres, substitute prescribing, advice, counselling and support. With the increased incidence of drug taking, primary health care teams have become more and more involved in treatment and support. Local authorities have always been expected to work with drug misusers and direct services are provided by the staff of social work departments in their day-to-day contact with drug misusers and their families. Many services are delivered from an addictions base using staff expert in alcohol misuse problems as well as drug misuse issues. Community-based services such as counselling and advice centres and community drugs projects, etc are provided either directly by social work departments or by the voluntary sector organisations funded by them. The voluntary sector contribution to the network of services and facilities currently available in Scotland has been substantial and vital; in particular it is a significant provider of both residential and community-based services. Social work departments and voluntary sector agencies also provide services for drugs misusers in prison or subject to community-based criminal justice sanctions.

4.3 From the reports submitted to the Drugs Task Force by Health Board General Managers and the Directors of Social Work Departments it is clear that a wide range of services for drug misusers exists in most health board and local authority areas. These include hospital based in-patient detoxification beds, and outpatient clinics, other residential detoxification/rehabilitation facilities, community-based advice and counselling services, community drugs projects, needle exchange schemes, family/self-help support groups, drop-in centres, and outreach services. Detoxification and in-patient care are mostly provided in hospital settings although the health boards also use facilities provided by the voluntary and independent sectors and make use of out of area referrals. The Drugs Task Force welcomes the opening this year of crisis intervention centres in Edinburgh and Glasgow, in both instances jointly funded by the health boards and local authority social work departments. These centres will provide immediate assistance and short-term residential care for drug misusers who have acute medical or social crises; they are a welcome addition to the range of services provided. **We are aware that crisis intervention centres are being considered for Aberdeen and Dundee and we would encourage the agencies concerned to develop their proposals as quickly as possible.**

4.4   The network of services available, particularly in the larger urban areas of Scotland, span the range recommended by ACMD although the provision of services in some of the rural parts of the country present particular problems and challenges and these require to be addressed by the health boards and local authorities concerned. It is encouraging that such a wide range of services is available and that the development of particular initiatives such as structured substitute prescribing arrangements (see 4.12 to 4.24 below) has been taken forward in Scotland. Drug misuse takes many forms and leads to a wide range of problems, of varying severity, for different groups of people. It is clearly important that the pattern of services provided in Scotland should be sufficiently adaptable to cater for drug misusers in a wide variety of circumstances and in both urban and rural communities. While no single pattern of service can suit such diversity, the aim must be to produce a comprehensive and co-ordinated network of support embracing both residential and community-based facilities. In recognising that drug services have developed on a "piecemeal" basis reflecting the way in which the drug misuse problem has increased and evolved, **we are clear that future service development must be based on a systematic and comprehensive assessment of the nature, extent and distribution of need. This assessment should be carried out by both health boards and social work departments reporting to the area Drug Action Teams described in Chapter 7.** In assessing needs, and the extent to which they are met, health boards and social work departments will require to take account of other service providers, including, for example, voluntary organisations. The views of drug misusers should also be taken into account in the needs assessment process in order to ensure that service provision is focused and relevant. Needs assessment should be an ongoing activity so that services can be adjusted to changing patterns of drug misuse.

EFFECTIVENESS OF SERVICES

4.5   There is pressure from drug misusers and their families for more residential care provision. For many drug misusers residential accommodation for respite care and health recovery, providing a concentrated period of personal support and assistance away from community pressures, is an essential part of the recovery process. While we recognise the importance of residential facilities, even after an intensive residential detoxification and recovery programme, many drug misusers find that, on return to their old environment and social pressures, they also return to their old drug misusing behaviour. Consequently, some professionals contend that treatment and care can more effectively be provided in the community. On this, our view is that services need to suit the individual. Each drug misuser has his or her own needs. These will vary over time and may call for different combinations of residential and non-residential services as part of a planned but flexible throughcare programme. It is essential that residential services are not seen in isolation from other health and social care services but rather as an integral component in the continuum of care, capable of complementing and supporting other services in the network. To make an effective contribution residential provision must be sufficiently varied to match the range of individual need, whether at the point of entry to services, during the recovery programme or following relapse. A particular feature of programmes will be their focus on joint work with community-based agencies to prepare for the resident's return to the community and ensure that adequate support is available when they leave.

4.6   In terms of treatment and social care programmes across the whole spectrum of services, whether hospital, residential or community-based, Drug Action Teams require not only to identify gaps in provision but to know what works, where, when and for whom. We recognise that this presents difficulties, but it is essential to have a clear view on effectiveness in order to assess what adjustments need to be made locally in the range and extent of services provided. The Drugs Task Force believes that much more work needs to be done at national level so that best practice can be identified and promoted across the country. **We recommend that the proposed Scottish advisory committee (see Chapter 7) should establish a sub-group of experts to advise on the effectiveness of various types of provision, including advice on what type of service, or**

combination of services, suits which type of misuser. The sub-group should take account of any relevant recommendations emerging from the review of the effectiveness of services for drug misusers in England, being undertaken by a Task Force led by the Rev Dr John Polkinghorne. Advice on the effectiveness of services will enable Drug Action Teams to form a view on the adequacy or otherwise of existing provision, including residential provision, in the light of their assessment of need. However, we stress that in the period until this further advice is issued, the local evaluation of services should not be consigned to the back burner. In the purchaser/provider climate in which health boards and social work departments now operate, there is ample scope for purchasers to ensure that, in drawing up contract specifications, the purchasers and the providers are clear about what is expected from whom and to ensure that service performance and outcomes are adequately monitored and evaluated.

THE IMPLEMENTATION OF COMMUNITY CARE

4.7 Following the implementation in full from 1 April 1993 of the National Health Service and Community Care Act 1990, local authorities are responsible for the care of vulnerable people with social care needs including people with alcohol and drug problems and their families. Under these new arrangements Social Work Departments have the lead responsibility for assessing the needs of drug users and for arranging services. They have also assumed responsibility from the Department of Social Security for the purchasing of residential and nursing home care for drug misusers (other than those with continuing health needs). The principal aims of the community care arrangements are to move from a service-led to a needs-led approach. Assessment of the individual is the key, and the intent is to provide services which promote choice and independence, that respond flexibly and sensitively to needs, and that intervene no more than necessary. Joint planning and co-ordinated provision by social work, health, educational and criminal justice agencies are central to these goals. Under these arrangements social work departments have the lead responsibility for developing and publishing community care plans, for assessing the social care needs of drug users and for arranging appropriate services.

4.8 The Social Work Services Group (SWSG) of The Scottish Office

Home and Health Department issued a circular in July 1993 to local authorities providing guidance about the issues which local authorities should consider in planning and providing services for those with drug problems. The Drugs Task Force welcomes the issue of this circular and the decision by SWSG to commission follow-up monitoring by Professor John Davies of Strathclyde University to determine progress made by local authorities in implementing the new arrangements. A number of the reports submitted to the Drugs Task Force by Directors of Social Work enclosed extracts from their Community Care Plans covering their departments' intentions with regard to services for drug misusers. While it is clear that considerable effort has gone into defining the needs and services required, a number of plans are less explicit about how these services are going to be delivered. **We recommend that Drug Action Teams should take the lead in ensuring that arrangements are in place locally to monitor the extent to which services are meeting the needs of drug misusers. Drug Action Teams should stimulate the development of services; and they should ensure that services are systematically reviewed.**

DEVELOPING THE VOLUNTARY SECTOR

4.9   The Drugs Task Force values the key role which the voluntary sector has played, and continues to play, in the provision of a wide range of services for drug misusers including community-based services such as counselling and advice, and residential facilities. Many drug misusers, particularly those with children, are particularly comfortable with voluntary organisations which they perceive to be non-judgemental and supportive in the services which they provide. It is clear from the reports submitted to the Drugs Task Force that, in general, good relationships exist in Scotland between local authorities, health boards and the voluntary sector in the planning, purchasing and provision of services for drug misusers. In particular the statutory agencies have been a source of regular funding for the voluntary sector both in purchasing their services and, in some cases, in providing core funding for their activities over a number of years. **Many voluntary organisations have shown themselves to be responsive and flexible to the needs of drug misusers and the Drugs Task Force considers it vital that the voluntary sector should be given every opportunity to develop and expand.** We recognise that the voluntary sector has understandable concerns about future funding arrangements; about contracts for services and evaluation; and about the need to be involved in the planning process. These issues are discussed in Chapter 7.

4.10 Since 1986 the Scottish Drugs Forum (SDF) has played an important role in bringing together voluntary sector organisations working in the field of drug misuse and in articulating the views and experiences of those working to tackle drug misuse. The SDF's core funding is provided by The Scottish Office but it also receives funding from a number of sources, including health boards, for the work it undertakes. Its activities include organising seminars; supporting the work of drug workers' groups; producing information materials; initiating and undertaking needs assessment surveys; and undertaking service development work. The SDF is performing a most valuable role in co-ordinating and stimulating action and it is capable of making an important contribution to the revised arrangements for co-ordinating local and national action which we propose in Chapter 7.

INITIATIVES IN COMMUNITY-BASED SERVICES

4.11 The importance of community-based services is reflected in the scale and range of community services for drug misusers across the country. Initiatives such as the home detoxification programme for drug misusers being developed in Ayrshire and Arran and in Central Region, and the drop-in centre for female prostitutes in Glasgow, are examples of the many worthwhile projects being undertaken. However, it is clear that there is scope for the further development of services to match the increasing misuse of drugs and commensurately the needs of drug misusers. While the traditional approach of rehabilitation, direct-contact counselling, group-work, etc is likely to remain the cornerstone of service provision, other approaches require to be developed. **There is clearly a need for innovation and we would urge the statutory and non-statutory agencies concerned with the provision of services to be bold in the promotion of innovative strategies.** In particular drug programmes offering alternative activities, education and, if possible, occupation to avoid drug-centred lifestyles seem well worth pursuing. Former drug misusers and indeed those on treatment programmes are not untrainable or unemployable because of their drug problem. Wherever possible the promotion of life opportunities viruses for drug misusers should be developed by tapping into existing services or by adopting approaches such as that of the APEX Trust, which provides opportunities for offenders to find employment or training opportunities. In paragraph 4.6 we describe the need to determine what works in the provision of services. Clearly similar considerations apply in the context of community-based initiatives. **Accordingly we recommend that the Scottish advisory committee should take stock of initiatives undertaken in developing community-based services with a view to developing, funding and evaluating further pilot projects and disseminating information on the most effective and worthwhile approaches.**

SUBSTITUTE PRESCRIBING

4.12 As we have previously noted, one of the key features of drug misuse in Scotland is the high incidence of injecting. Injecting drug misuse is particularly hazardous to health. There has been a substantial number of cases in Glasgow in recent years (discussed in Chapter 5) in which injecting drug misuse has led directly to death. In Scotland there has also been a particularly close association between the sharing of injecting equipment and the spread of HIV. What is perhaps less well understood are the many more common health risks associated with unhygienic injecting activity which is prevalent amongst this group. Some of these include septicaemia, septic thrombophlebitis, pulmonary embolism, gangrene, and cellulitis. Moreover, in addition to HIV, other serious public health threats arise from injecting such as the spread of the Hepatitis B, C and D viruses. A number of these conditions have long-term consequences and may indeed be life threatening.

4.13 Accordingly, steps to tackle injecting drug misuse have rightly had a high priority in Scotland. Two measures of particular relevance have been the introduction of needle exchange arrangements which seek to minimise the harm to health which injecting can cause; and the approach known as substitute prescribing. Both of these have raised some controversy. When the first needle and syringe exchange schemes were introduced in April 1987 there was a degree of disquiet amongst the general public and within the professions. However, the careful arrangements under which these schemes operate have led to widespread acceptance of their value, both in helping to reduce the spread of HIV and in attracting misusers to services. Similar concerns have surrounded substitute prescribing.

Some perceive substitute prescribing as simply providing another drug to misusers in place of the drug of dependency. Others are concerned that it is a social control mechanism for the drug misusing population.

4.14 As practised in Scotland, substitute prescribing involves the prescribing of non-injectable drugs such as oral methadone to those who have become dependent on drugs obtained illicitly. There are both medical and social benefits arising from such an approach even if the ultimate objective of enabling a persistent misuser to become drug-free is not achieved until a number of years have passed. Medically the use of oral methadone should reduce the incidence of injecting with its particularly damaging health consequences. Moreover the provision of a drug of consistent composition should avert some of the dangers to health which arise from the use of street drugs of varying purity and quality. Socially the provision of prescribed drugs should contribute to stabilising the misuser's lifestyle. The tasks of searching out sources of drug supply, and of obtaining the money to enable drugs to be bought, should no longer dominate the misuser's life. Potentially there are also benefits for society in terms of a reduction both in the illicit drugs market and in the amount of crime committed by drug misusers to obtain funds to buy drugs. **Substitute prescribing, therefore, is a facilitator through which drug misusers can be brought within a framework of care which benefits the individual and society.**

4.15 There are various ways in which substitute prescribing can be delivered: independently by GPs in the normal course of their patient care; by specialist hospital based services; and by shared care arrangements through GPs and specialists working in a co-ordinated service. Under the shared care arrangements (as for example developed by the Community Drug Problem Service in Lothian over the last 5 years), GPs are supported by drug misuse specialist services (consultants, psychiatric nurses, community nurses, social workers and other community based drug services) in a multi-disciplinary approach. The advantage is that this enables a wide range of services to be delivered to the drug misuser and thus enhances the potential effect of substitute prescribing in achieving behavioural change.

4.16 The number of methadone prescriptions in Scotland increased from 6594 in 1988 to 89,867 in 1993. The Lothian Community Drug Problem Service, which was established in 1988, has taken the lead in Scotland in promoting the substitute prescribing approach and in developing a framework of services within which substitute prescribing is delivered. A number of other health boards in Scotland have developed Community Drug Problem Services based, in whole or in part, on the Lothian model. Most recently the Greater Glasgow Health Board introduced in early 1994 its own Drug Problem Service which draws on practice in Lothian.

4.17 As to the impact of substitute prescribing in Scotland, there is certainly persuasive evidence that the CDPS approach has had an effect on injecting behaviour. In the year ending 31 March 1993 out of 584 drug misusers coming to the notice of services in Lothian for the first time (as reported to the Scottish Drug Misuse Database) only 33 (or 6%) were injectors. By comparison, in Greater Glasgow 898 (or 63%) of the 1418 misusers coming to notice were injectors. The number of deaths as a direct result of drug misuse (see Chapter 5) is also lower in Edinburgh than in Glasgow.

4.18 Substitute prescribing was endorsed by the ACMD in its 1988 report "AIDS and Drug Misuse" and in its 1993 report "AIDS and Drug Misuse Update". The 1993 report stressed the need for structured programmes with frequent client/counsellor contact and a regular review of each client's treatment goal. The ACMD emphasised that maintenance programmes should have routes for referral to in-patient and out-patient detoxification and for gradual "maintenance to abstinence" programmes. Substitute prescribing has also been endorsed by the Government's Chief Medical Officers in "Drug Misuse and Dependence - Guidelines on Clinical Management", issued in 1991, as "a useful tool, where appropriate, in helping to change the behaviour of some drug misusers either towards abstinence or towards intermediate goals such as a reduction in injecting or sharing of injecting equipment." The Scottish Affairs Select Committee, in their recent report on drug abuse in Scotland, also supported the principle of substitute prescribing.

4.19 The Drugs Task Force concurs with the views of the ACMD and the Scottish Affairs Committee in recognising the value of substitute prescribing. Although we are aware of the concerns of some sections of the medical profession on medical and ethical grounds, in our view substitute prescribing has an important contribution to make in tackling drug misuse, particularly injecting drug misuse, in Scotland. The very high level of injecting in Scotland underlines the importance of having measures in place which will have an impact on reducing this dangerous practice. Providing oral substitutes as a means of attracting the injecting population into services as the first step on the road to recovery is, therefore, a practical means of achieving this aim. We would however wish to make several important points about the framework within which substitute prescribing should be provided.

4.20 First, we commend the CDPS arrangements whereby a partnership is established between GPs and a specialised central service. Most, if not all, GPs treating persistent drug misusers need the support, advice and access to services which specialist help can provide; they should not be expected to go it alone. On the other hand, we are keen to ensure that the GP should continue to play a full part in the medical treatment of drug misusers and should not simply transfer the responsibility to a central service. This would tend both to stigmatise the drug misuser and distort his or her pattern of medical care. The partnership approach, as in the CDPS model, seems to us to be the right way forward. In some other areas of Scotland GPs have been keen to transfer responsibility for drug misusers to a central service. We urge health boards, through persuasion and encouragement, to ensure that a true partnership is achieved.

4.21 Second, we would emphasise that substitute prescribing should not be delivered in isolation from other services. It should be part - a key part but nonetheless only one part - of a coherent approach to delivering services to drug misusers. The full potential of substitute prescribing will only be realised if it is delivered as part of a package of services, which embraces not only medical but also the social care services, including community-based drug services. We consider that the social work input into medically-led services should be strengthened. The value of the multi-agency approach whereby services for drug misusers are delivered as a coherent and co-ordinated totality of provision cannot be over-emphasised. **We recommend that the Community Drug Problem Service model should be further developed with a view to achieving more referrals from and to generic social work services. We recommend also that the model should be developed with a view to providing additional support to, and obtaining the assistance of, the families of drug misusers.** The pervasive effect of drug misuse extends beyond the misuser and, indeed, family members may have a vital role to play, with the right professional support, in efforts to control or reverse drug misuse behaviour. **Further, we**

recommend that the model should be developed with a view to reaching drug misusers at an earlier point in their drug careers. At present those referred to services tend to have a lengthy history of drug misuse, although there are some signs that this is reducing. We think that the CDPS model should take on a more proactive edge in making contact with those in need of services. A closer relationship with generic social work services, and liaison with voluntary agencies in contact with drug misusers, would facilitate this.

4.22 Third, we emphasise the need to match the services provided to the circumstances of the individual drug misuser. There should be no presumption, on the part of the patient or the prescriber, that the substitute prescription approach is always the best way of dealing with persistent injecting drug misuse. There is a clear requirement for a thorough assessment of the needs of the individual drug misuser in each case before entering into any treatment and care regime. Where substitute prescribing is part of such a package there should be an agreed contract between the doctor and the individual drug misuser which outlines the structured arrangement within which the programme will be undertaken. It must be recognised that drug misuse is a chronically relapsing condition, but for those providing care for drug misusers the ultimate goal of abstinence should always be kept in mind. Experience has shown that substitute prescribing may have to be provided in many cases over a long period, before the goal of abstinence is achieved. Substitute drugs should be prescribed in limited quantities and the dosage, and all other aspects of the treatment and care, should be reviewed regularly. In those cases where it is necessary to maintain misusers on a constant level of the prescribed drug for a prolonged period, the goal of reduction, and ultimately of abstinence should be kept to the fore. We regard this as vital in the interests not only of the patient but also in order to minimise the leakage of prescribed drugs onto the illicit market.

4.23 We are aware of the care with which the Community Drug Problem Services established in Scotland approach the issues of prescribing. Nevertheless, for the benefit of health boards introducing similar services, it is worth emphasising the importance of tight controls over substitute prescribing. **We believe that there is now sufficient experience of operating substitute prescribing in Scotland to enable more specific guidelines on prescription practices to be drawn up and we recommend that this should be put in hand, for**

the benefit of the ever increasing number of doctors faced with prescription decisions in these circumstances. We also recommend that independent and objective monitoring of those Scottish drugs services which incorporate substitute prescribing should be conducted with a view to further identifying good practice in the delivery of services, including an assessment of effectiveness in controlling and changing drug use behaviour.

4.24 Finally we would emphasise that our endorsement of substitute prescribing applies only to the prescription of drugs for oral use. We are aware that, internationally, some clinicians are prepared to contemplate the prescription of substitute drugs in an injectable form but in Scottish circumstances, given the high incidence of injecting drug misuse here, we would regard any such action as going beyond what is acceptable.

THE ROLE OF GPS

4.25 For many drug misusers the first professional they are likely to encounter who can offer help with their problem will be their GP whom they will see either because they have symptoms relating to their drug use or because of other health problems. It is important that patients should feel able to "open up" to their GP about their drug dependency in the knowledge that they will be treated sympathetically and given the necessary help. GPs have a key role in the diagnosis of drug misuse, early intervention, advice and treatment. In a substantial number of patients drug misuse decreases over time, and if the patient can be kept healthy through the skilled management of his problem by his GP this greatly assists the process of recovery. There is encouraging evidence that many doctors provide a high level of care for patients with drug misuse problems. Specialist nurses based in general practices can also provide considerable assistance to GPs in the monitoring and care of drug misuser patients. The Drugs Task Force agrees with the views expressed in various ACMD Reports and in the Scottish Affairs Committee report about the crucial role of GPs in the treatment of drug misusers. We are pleased to hear that a significant number of Glasgow GPs have contracted with Greater Glasgow Health Board to run special drug misuse clinics for registered opiate addicts outside the normal scope of General Medical Services. These arrangements offer a pointer which other boards may wish to consider.

4.26 However, the Drugs Task Force recognises that many GPs are unhappy about taking on drug misusers as some may disrupt their clinics, upset staff and other patients, and may be extremely time consuming. GPs operating without the backup of the kind of specialist and multi-disciplinary support offered by a CDPS type service, may feel isolated and lack the training, the confidence and the knowledge to treat drug misusers. Guidance and support must be provided to GPs in these circumstances. The advice in "Drug Misuse and Dependence: Guidelines on Clinical Management" which was issued to all doctors in Scotland in December 1991, is particularly helpful in this connection. In relation to substitute prescribing, the more specific guidelines which we have recommended at para 4.23 may also be helpful. **But we recognise that further action to support GPs may be necessary, at both local and national level. This is a matter which we recommend the proposed Scottish advisory committee should keep under close review.**

4.27 Training is also very important and we believe that an educational initiative for all doctors and medical students in the treatment and care of drug misusers would have a positive effect in bringing them on board. Accordingly the Drugs Task Force has arranged in consultation with the Scottish Council for Postgraduate Medical and Dental Education for a series of educational initiatives to be held around Scotland to encourage doctors to become involved in the treatment of drug misusers.

4.28 Initial training on drug misuse must also be given to medical students. The first exposure to the problem of drug misuse which a junior house doctor often experiences is when a misuser arrives on a hospital ward in crisis and the doctor's lack of experience is exposed. This is clearly unsatisfactory. Doctors must be equipped with the attitude, skills and knowledge to be comfortable in dealing with the issues surrounding drug misuse. **We recommend that The Scottish Office should pursue with the Deans of the Medical Schools how enhanced training in dealing with drug misuse might be provided during the undergraduate training of medical students.**

OUTREACH

4.29 If a significant impact is to be made on the serious problem of drug misuse in Scotland it will be essential to make early contact with drug misusers. Outreach work will be vital in this regard. The ACMD in its "AIDS and Drug Misuse Update" report devoted an entire chapter to the role and importance of outreach work. The objective of outreach work is to target individuals and groups who do not seek access to existing services and to work with them in their own communities and local settings for the purposes of improving their health and reducing any harm they may be doing to themselves through risky drug using practices. Detached outreach work in Scotland has been developing since 1985 but there appears to be continuing confusion about what it is, where it should happen and best practice. Outreach work clearly needs to take place where young people congregate - that is to say on the streets, on station concourses, in pubs, bars and cafes. Peripatetic outreach focuses on organisations rather than individuals and the work undertaken is often in hostels, needle and syringe exchanges, youth clubs, etc. There may also be a need for domiciliary outreach focusing on visiting the homes of target populations. We believe that much of the best practice in this area is to be found in the non-statutory sector, probably because the managers of outreach workers in the non-statutory sector have direct experience of detached/outreach work themselves and therefore recognise the challenges faced by outreach staff.

4.30   The importance of attracting young people to drug services at an early stage in their drug taking careers has arisen in many of our discussions at Drugs Task Force meetings. Outreach workers offer the best prospects for success in contacting hard-to-reach groups and bringing them into contact with service structures. However outreach workers are operating in a difficult environment often with an insufficient focus on their objectives. **We therefore recommend that the agencies employing outreach workers should establish clear objectives and standards of practice for outreach workers and ensure that they are well supported at management level.** The Drugs Task Force recognises that outreach workers and the agencies which employ them are often faced with difficult situations surrounding harm reduction issues primarily where they relate to drug misusers under 16. The circumstances in which the issuing of condoms or giving advice about safer drug misusing practices may arise require sensitive handling and the exercise of sound judgement. Outreach workers need the support and assurance of their managers in dealing with these difficult matters.

"RECREATIONAL" DRUG MISUSE

4.31   While cannabis and other drugs such as Ecstasy, used on a so called recreational basis, are generally acknowledged to be non-addictive they can sometimes lead to the use of other drugs as well as being harmful to health. However, whether we like it or not, many young people seem to take the view that this kind of drug use is not a problem but simply part of life. They take drugs on an occasional basis because it makes them feel good and they enjoy the experience. There can be little doubt that most young people are well aware of the risks they run in terms of the illegality of their activities. Given this perception by young people the present drug services, which are geared predominantly to opiate misuse, are not seen, in general, as relevant to their needs. The difficulty is determining an appropriate strategy for responding to the use of recreational drugs by young people. The challenge must be to divert them away from the attractions of recreational drug use. What is required are alternative activities which engage young people at a time in their lives when they are attracted by excitement and risk. **We recognise that this is a very difficult area but we recommend that the development of alternative activities which seek to engage young people should be pursued in the pilot community drug action schemes referred to at para 3.38 above.**

4.32   Deaths have regrettably occurred from the misuse of Ecstasy (MDMA) including, in recent months, a number in Scotland. In common with other amphetamines, MDMA can cause psychiatric trauma but does not produce major physical withdrawal symptoms. The deaths which have occurred result from a range of reactions including acute renal failure, hyperthermia and convulsions. The use of Ecstasy combined with the high ambient temperatures associated with "rave" events, sustained physical activity and inadequate fluid intake, provides a combination of circumstances which, as events have shown, can prove fatal. A further worrying development is the evidence from drug projects that some young people who use Ecstasy subsequently resort to other controlled drugs such as Temazepam to counter the after effects of the Ecstasy. Young people must be made aware of the risks of these dangerous practices.

4.33   While "raves" are held to attract young people to a particular vogue in music and dance - and many young people attend them for that reason only - we recognise that they are also an environment where drug taking does occur. Raves are held on a regular basis around

Scotland and the policy has generally been to try to handle them under controlled conditions and therefore subject to the requirements of the Licensing (Scotland) Act 1976 and of the Civic Government (Scotland) Act 1982. While we believe this to be a sound approach, the Drugs Task Force considers it vital that everything possible is done to ensure that rave events are as safe as they can be for young people. **The Task Force does not condone the misuse of drugs at raves and expects the organisers, in association with the police service, to take all practicable steps to deal with the problem effectively.** Recognising however that drug misuse may continue to be a feature of raves, we have concerns relating to matters such as the appropriate levels of stewarding, the availability of paramedic staff, the provision of "chill-out" areas and free accessible water, and the availability of information on the risks which attach to Ecstasy use and harm-minimisation issues. Comprehensive guidance covering issues such as crowd safety, venue standards, stewarding, medical aid and welfare services, and the provision of refreshments and drinking water, etc already exists in the "Guide to Health, Safety and Welfare at Pop Concerts and Similar Events" published jointly by the Health and Safety Commission, the Home Office and The Scottish Office in October 1993. This guidance is however directed primarily towards pop concerts and other similar outdoor events rather than indoor events normally held at discotheques or night clubs. **We recommend therefore that The Scottish Office should issue separate guidance for local authorities and licensing boards to bring to the attention of organisers of such indoor events. Such guidance would cover the areas of concern we have identified above.**

4.34 We have also considered whether conditions bearing on the type of drug misuse which occurs at rave events might be attached to licences, though we recognise that responding to these problems through the licensing system is not straightforward. The Civic Government (Scotland) Act 1982 gives licensing authorities a wide discretion to attach "such reasonable conditions as [they] think fit" to rave events which are subject to a public entertainment licence under section 41 of the Act. Such a licence is in general however appropriate only where the organisers are not selling alcohol. Where rave events are to be held in premises in which alcohol is to be on sale, the relevant licence is normally an entertainment licence granted under the Licensing (Scotland) Act 1976. Licensing boards have certain powers to attach conditions to such licences under the 1976 Act. **We recommend that The Scottish Office, in consultation** with the police, local authorities, licensing boards and other relevant interests should examine the extent to which it might be practicable and useful for model licensing conditions reflecting the areas of concern we have mentioned to be prepared for use by local authorities and licensing boards according to circumstances pertaining in their areas.

NEEDLE AND SYRINGE EXCHANGE SCHEMES

4.35 Needle and syringe exchange schemes have a vital role in combating the spread of HIV, Hepatitis B, C and D amongst injecting drug misusers, and have come to be recognised as an essential element in prevention and harm minimisation strategies. Such schemes serve not only to ensure a ready supply of sterile injecting equipment, thus reducing the risk of needle sharing, but also provide a suitable setting for the provision of a whole range of services, including harm minimisation advice, safer sex counselling, child care and health care promotion as well as a level of primary health care. Under existing arrangements, schemes provided under the National Health Service are approved by The Scottish Office and must satisfy both the Lord Advocate's guidelines and conditions laid down by the Department. There are restrictions on the number of equipment sets which can be distributed on any one occasion, and the issue of further supplies of 'works' is dependent on the return of used equipment. This carefully controlled development of exchanges has been justified in practice. In particular, the high return rate of used equipment has been a notable feature, while the extensive groundwork undertaken before new schemes are established has resulted in exchanges achieving a high degree of acceptance in the neighbourhoods in which they are located. Research indicates that high risk behaviour such as needle sharing and the passing on of used 'works' has declined since needle and syringe exchange services became available. Currently, there are 23 exchanges, mainly in the cities.

4.36 In addition to these freestanding exchanges, regulations introduced in 1992 have enabled certain community pharmacies to distribute syringes to clients free of charge, and some 88 pharmacies throughout Scotland are now offering this service. General medical practitioners can also - and helpfully do - supply injecting equipment to patients presenting with drug problems.

4.37 Needle and syringe exchange schemes have clearly demonstrated their worth and the Task Force has considered, in the light of evidence it has received and the views of the Scottish Affairs Committee, whether the present arrangements might be enhanced. The Scottish Affairs Committee noted that, despite the success of the existing exchanges, it appeared that some injectors never attended the services and were dependent on 'secondary' suppliers among their friends. The Committee observed that drug misusers in rural areas faced particular difficulties in obtaining needles and syringes because of the closely knit nature of the community. Noting that the existing guidelines restricted the supply of needles and syringes, save in exceptional circumstances, to 10 sets per person, the Committee took the view that there could be occasions where relaxation of this limit could be justified on public health grounds and that, provided there was the strictest of control and monitoring, drug workers in needle exchanges should be given discretion to increase the number of sets distributed at any one time. The Committee also recommended that careful consideration should be given to extending the range of outlets for the supply of clean injecting equipment to drug injectors.

4.38 Similar representations have been made to the Drugs Task Force and to The Scottish Office. The current restrictions on the number of equipment sets which can be issued on any one occasion mean that frequent injectors may need to visit exchanges several times a week; this is obviously a disincentive and may lead to the re-use or sharing of needles. The problem is particularly acute where the injector lives at a distance from an exchange and the cost and time of the journey adds to the disincentive effect.

4.39 In the Drugs Task Force's view these difficulties do not justify the removal altogether of the restrictions on the operation of exchanges, which must continue to operate within a defined framework incorporating an upper limit on the number of sets of equipment which may be issued. **However we do see some scope for raising the current upper limit. We have conveyed these views to the Lord Advocate and we are glad to hear that it has now been agreed to increase the number of sets which may be issued on the second and subsequent visits to an exchange from 10 to 15 (providing the quantity issued on the previous occasion is returned safely for disposal). In exceptional cases - for example, when a client is collecting equipment on behalf of a spouse or where there are particular difficulties in rural situations - the upper limit will be raised to 30.** The Drugs Task Force is confident that these adjustments will help meet current difficulties and enhance the already significant contribution made by the exchanges.

4.40 Raising the upper limit will help to alleviate the problems faced by injectors in rural areas. But the Task Force considers that there is a need for additional measures, especially in areas where exchanges are remote from pockets of need. We therefore propose that, building on the concept of outreach work which we have discussed earlier, selected exchange staff or other qualified personnel might make home visits to carefully identified injectors in rural areas to distribute and collect needles and syringes. Particular care will need to be taken in selecting clients to minimise any risk or danger to the personnel concerned; and it would be a condition that counselling, advice and any other appropriate services is made available to the clients. **To test this initiative, we recommend that a few carefully selected pilot schemes should be introduced on a trial basis, with a view to considering whether the practice might be adopted more widely.**

THE ROLE OF PHARMACEUTICAL SERVICES

4.41 Pharmacists play an important role in providing services for drug misusers. Needle and syringe exchange services are well established in 88 community pharmacies in Scotland and dispensing prescriptions for patients receiving substitute therapy is an expanding area. They are well placed to offer counselling and advice not only on general health care matters and safer sex but also on issues specific to the individual. Pharmacists are making an important contribution to the Community Drug Problem Services. As a member of the health care team, the pharmacist can also provide drug information to health care professionals, including advice on security, and safety of drugs. **In the Drugs Task Force's view there is considerable potential for pharmacists to play an even greater role in "frontline" services to drug misusers. We recommend that health boards consider how best this can be developed.** For pharmacists to play their full role it will be necessary to ensure that all their training requirements are met.

WOMEN AND DRUG MISUSE

4.42 The Drugs Task Force considered the issues surrounding women and drug misuse throughout our deliberations. It was considered, however, that women's issues merited special mention in recognition of its importance as a subject in its own right. All too often the special needs of women in many spheres of life go unrecognised and this cannot be allowed to happen in the drug misuse field. Drug misuse amongst women tends to be even more hidden than amongst the rest of the general population and information on prevalence is scarce. However, drug misusing women are by no means a new phenomenon, although they are more difficult to contact. Critics have contended that treatment facilities are often insensitive to the unique needs of the female drug misuser. Attitudes towards female drug misusers have been forged largely from stereo-types, information is based upon the experience of male drug misusers, and scientific literature has focused almost exclusively on male drug misusers. The issues of drug misuse in women cannot be addressed without an understanding of the fundamental role that gender plays in defining individual identity, coping style and skills, structure of a person's life style, and the nature of life experience, including the psychological and social realities which women face. For example, one of the underlying issues for women who misuse drugs is that of abusive, violent relationships and low self-esteem.

4.43   ACMD in its AIDS and Drug Misuse Part 2 report published in 1989 recommended that special efforts were required to maximise contact with women who misuse drugs, and services were required to provide women only sessions, access to women doctors and counsellors, together with provision of child care and family planning facilities. Some helpful developments along this path have taken place in Scotland through the work of Dr Mary Hepburn in Glasgow in providing an obstetric service for women who are drug dependent. **We recommend that all female drug misusers, particularly pregnant women and women with children, should have access to regular, sensitive counselling, support and information.**

4.44   Residential recovery facilities such as those provided by the Aberlour Child Care Trust in Edinburgh and Glasgow for women (with their children) who have drug and alcohol problems are an important aspect of service provision. **We recommend that the Drug Action Teams should examine the need for women-only residential provision (which would enable women to remain with their children if they so wish) in their areas.**

4.45   Almost inevitably the cultural attitudes that assume that certain types of behaviour are less acceptable in women than in men permeate the drugs field. Where these attitudes exist they must be examined, challenged and changed. It is important for service providers to ensure that they do not fall into the trap of stereo-typing women drug misusers and that women are actively involved in the planning, development and provision of services. Research suggests that although proportionally fewer female than male drug misusers attend drug services, those services which make particular efforts to gear what is offered to the needs of women can be successful in attracting a much higher proportion of women clients. Drug services should review their policies to ensure that they are receptive to the needs of women. **Accordingly we recommend that the agencies concerned should review their services for women drug misusers (including child care needs) and, in particular, consult their women clients for their views on the services offered and encourage them to be involved in the long term monitoring and evaluation of service provision with the aim of developing a more attractive service to women drug misusers.**

DRUG MISUSE AND THE ETHNIC MINORITIES

4.46 Few members of the ethnic minorities (who account for 1% of the Scottish population) seek help from drug agencies. It would be wrong to assume that this means that there is no problem among this section of the community. The reasons for the low level of referrals are likely to include religious and cultural barriers, racial concerns, possible language problems and worries about confidentiality. As with women drug misusers, **we recommend that providers should ensure that their services are "user-friendly" to members of the ethnic minorities and that they are capable of recognising and addressing possible barriers to the effective provision of services to those who need them.**

CONCLUSION

4.47 Finally, we emphasise that those providing services - whether directly addressing drug misusers' needs, or strengthening the capacities of individuals and communities to resist drug misuse - need to be aware of the importance of service presentation. If barriers exist between those who provide services and those who misuse drugs - or contemplate their misuse - then the impact of those services will be greatly impaired. If services are not accessible or acceptable to misusers they will not be effective. We would also stress the importance of maintaining involvement and contact with misusers, even if the outcomes of that involvement are imperceptible, and the contact is difficult to sustain. If contact is lost, opportunities for intervention diminish and risk - including risk to life - escalates.

5 DRUG DEATHS

5.1   According to figures collected by the police, during 1992 there were 71 drug-related deaths in Glasgow; in 1993 there were 41 deaths and in the first 9 months of 1994 there have been 48 deaths. A death is defined as a drug-related death where there is prima facie evidence of a fatal overdose of controlled drugs. Such evidence would be recent drug misuse, for example, controlled drugs and/or a hypodermic syringe found in close proximity to the body, and/or the person is known to the police as a drug misuser although not necessarily a notified addict. These deaths in Glasgow and the fact that the problem had not manifested itself to the same extent elsewhere in the country, engendered considerable and understandable public concern. This led subsequently to the Law Officers in Scotland instructing that a conjoined Fatal Accident Inquiry (FAI) should be held into the circumstances of 4 deaths which had features in common and were characteristic of the deaths reported and investigated over the past 2 years. The FAI was held on 1 and 2 November 1993 and the Sheriff returned formal verdicts citing drugs as the cause of death.

5.2   A number of experts were invited by the Procurator Fiscal in Glasgow to examine the circumstances surrounding these deaths and the Drugs Task Force has had an opportunity to consider their reports. The experts compared drug deaths in Edinburgh with those in Glasgow during 2 years, November 1990 to October 1991 (Year 1) and November 1991 to October 1992 (Year 2). During these periods there were 13 and 53 deaths, respectively, in Glasgow and 12 and 14 deaths, respectively, in Edinburgh. The drugs involved in these deaths are set out in the following table:–

TABLE 1

	Glasgow Year 1	Glasgow Year 2	Edinburgh Year 1	Edinburgh Year 2
Total deaths	13	53	12	14
Heroin present	10	41	1	1
Temazepam present	5	34	2	3
Diazepam present	1	23	-	2
Methadone present	-	2	2	11
Other drugs present	2	15	8	2
Alcohol present	2	20	2	1

Table 1 provides a breakdown of the drugs which were identified during the post-mortem examinations. It highlights the problem of polydrug use, showing that in many of the deaths a combination of various drugs were present. It also reveals that in both years heroin was associated with a large number of deaths. Temazepam and Diazepam figure heavily in the drug deaths in Glasgow usually as a secondary drug. The experts' reports also pointed out that Glasgow's overall population is less than double that of Edinburgh yet the drug deaths in 1992 were almost 4 times as many. This may, however, be accounted for by the larger number of injecting drug misusers in Glasgow compared with Edinburgh.

TABLE 2

AGE OF DEATH: GLASGOW DRUG DEATHS: NOVEMBER 1991-OCTOBER 1992 (YEAR 2)

Age Group	Male	Female	Total	%
Under 20	1	1	2	4
20-24	11	8	19	36
25-29	15	5	20	38
30-34	7	–	7	13
35+	3	1	4	7
Not known	1	–	1	2
Total	38	15	53	100

This loss of life is of great concern. Table 2 above shows that there were 38 men (72%) and 15 women (28%) who died; more of the women were aged under 25 (60%) than men (32%). The youngest who died was a man aged 18 and the oldest a man aged 39.

TABLE 3

PLACE OF DEATH: GLASGOW DRUG DEATHS: NOVEMBER 1991-OCTOBER 1992 (YEAR 2)

Place	No	Alone at Time of Death	With Other Users	Non-Users (ie in another part of house)
Home	34*	13	1	20
Home of Friend	8#	1	5	2
Public Place	11°	8	3	–
Totals	53	22	9	22

*2	from this category were moved to hospital and later died there
#2	from this category were moved to hospital and later died there
o1	from this category was moved to hospital and later died there

The places of death varied as Table 3 reveals. Those concerned lived in many parts of Glasgow but largely those characterised by significant economic and social problems.

5.3   While the circumstances surrounding the Glasgow deaths were not all the same there were very many striking similarities. Most of those who died were young (90% under 34 years of age), they were chaotic polydrug users and they injected. The intravenous injection of drugs produces a finer line between life and death than the oral consumption of drugs, which even in overdosage, allows more time for intervention before respiratory failure and cardiac arrest take place. The fact that some of the victims were discovered with the needles still in their bodies indicates that misjudgment of the body's tolerance was a significant factor.

5.4   The Scottish Affairs Committee report (paragraph 29) points out that fatal overdosing by drug injectors is the most important single cause of death among young adults in Glasgow. The Drugs Task Force regards this as an appalling situation which must be tackled vigorously by all the agencies involved. In our view, recent important policy developments offer the best long term prospects for reducing the number of drug deaths in Glasgow. These include the establishment of the Glasgow Drug Problem Service; and the opening of the Crisis Intervention Centre in Glasgow. **The development of a range of social care and health responses for drug misusers in Glasgow supported by inter-agency co-operation and planning should have an impact over time in reducing the high number of drug-related deaths in the city. The setting up of the multi-disciplinary Glasgow Drug Problem Service is particularly welcome.** This will provide a structured programme for drug misusers which, among other things, will aim to persuade drug misusers to change from the injection of street drugs to prescribed oral substitutes. While the Drugs Task Force recognises that the substitute prescribing policy adopted in Edinburgh has not succeeded in eliminating drug misuse, nor will it prevent every fatality, there is evidence that it is reducing some of the harm of drug misuse, it is reducing injecting, it is reducing street drug use and there are indications that it is also reducing drug-related crime. The Glasgow Drug Problem Service will be an important resource of best practice advice to GPs on treatment programmes for misusers covering, in particular, assessment, harm reduction, prescribing protocols and dealing with crises, and we wish it well.

5.5 While the arrangements described above provide the basis for a vigorous and sustained response to the drug misuse problem in Glasgow there is clearly a need for other pragmatic measures to be adopted to combat, in particular, the dangers of drug injection. The dangers associated with injecting and the high number of deaths have been seen as a particular problem in Glasgow but deaths of drug misusers from injecting and overdosing have also occurred elsewhere in Scotland. **Accordingly following discussions at Drugs Task Force meetings we have commissioned the Scottish Drugs Forum, through The Scottish Office, to develop information/publicity materials focusing on and directed at polydrug using injectors, highlighting these dangerous practices and providing commonsense advice on reducing the risks.** The material will be distributed to persistent drug misusers by detached outreach workers, through drug agencies and needle exchange schemes throughout Scotland. We believe this will be a helpful and worthwhile initiative.

5.6 A particularly pertinent issue which has emerged from our consideration of the Glasgow drug deaths is the number of occasions when those who died were described as being "in touch with services". Of the 53 deaths in Glasgow in the year from November 1991, 22 misusers were registered with health, social work or other services. In theory this should have increased the potential for offering some form of intervention before the individuals' drug-taking careers led to their deaths. It is self evident, however, that those who died had not been drawn sufficiently into the support network to the extent necessary to influence their behaviour. This underlines the importance of making early contact with drug misusers and engaging them sufficiently to influence potentially dangerous behaviour such as injecting and polydrug misuse. **Improved and increased outreach work in contacting hard-to-reach groups will undoubtedly help but we recommend that all the agencies involved should take steps to ensure that in their contacts with persistent drug misusers they continually emphasise the dangers of reckless injecting behaviour and polydrug misuse.** It is encouraging that in some areas of Scotland, such as Lothian where a large number of drug misusers have stopped injecting, drug misusers are taking steps to reduce the harm which injecting causes. We hope that a similar attitude will prevail in Glasgow now that a full range of services is available.

6 FUNDING

6.1   Responding to drug misuse consumes a substantial amount of resources across a range of services. The Scottish Office has estimated that in 1992-93 some £42m of public expenditure was spent on drug-related action in Scotland. This figure is based on an estimate of the resources which various services - the police, social work, education, health and prison services - devote to dealing with drug misuse as part of their general work, to which is added the cost of services specifically directed to drug misuse.

FUNDING SOURCES

6.2   The services provided for the treatment and care of drug misusers are funded from a variety of sources:–

(a)   *Hea th boards*

Health boards receive specific resources for drug misuse services in addition to their general allocations. Part of the specific funding goes to support services provided by the voluntary sector, and this may be routed through social work departments.

(b)   *Loca Authorities*

Local authorities' drug misuse services are generally funded through revenue support grant mechanisms, primarily channelled through community care budgets. In addition, The Scottish Office meets the full cost of social work services in the criminal justice system, many of which are targeted at drug misusing offenders.

(c) *Section 10 Funding*

The Scottish Office provides funding direct to voluntary bodies for worthwhile innovative projects, including those related to drug misuse, under section 10(1) of the Social Work (Scotland) Act 1968. This is administered by Social Work Services Group. Funding under section 10 is normally available for the first 2 to 3 years of a project's life to pilot a new approach or help to get it established. Grants are currently being made available to the Scottish Drugs Forum for a development officer and to Crew 2000 for its work with young drug misusers.

(d) *Section 16B Grant*

The Scottish Office provides funding to voluntary organisations under section 16B of the National Health Service (Scotland) Act 1978 as amended. The section 16B grant scheme is designed to assist national voluntary organisations whose aims are complementary to the health services which statute requires be provided. Grants are usually given to help with the administrative (core) cost of running their headquarters. Organisations such as the Scottish Drugs Forum and the Scottish AIDS Monitor are funded in this way.

(e) *Urban Aid Funding*

Central government has made extensive use of the Urban Programme to help local authorities target services on urban areas suffering most from severe multiple deprivation. The projects funded - which are often managed by voluntary organisations and community groups - tackle a wide range of social, economic and environmental issues. Moreover, many are targeted specifically on drug misusers and their families.

6.3   During the Task Force's work we have considered whether the current funding mechanisms are appropriate, whether there is sufficient ring-fencing of resources to safeguard services, and whether the balance between health board and local authority provision is appropriate. We have also examined how best to ensure that Urban Aid funded projects sponsored by local authorities are fully taken into account in planning drug misuse services. The remainder of this chapter examines these issues.

6.4   The specific resources provided to health boards for drug misuse services stem directly from a recommendation in the ACMD's 1982 report on Treatment and Rehabilitation that there should be increased funding direct from central government, possibly by way of pump priming grants, to enable new projects to be undertaken for the treatment and rehabilitation of drug misusers. For the first 3 years of their existence most of these funded projects were the direct responsibility of The Scottish Office, but in 1987, after evaluation, responsibility was transferred to the relevant health boards. The "earmarked" funding of these projects continued to be provided to health boards under the terms of NHS Circular 1987(GEN)6. Most of the money made available to health boards via GEN6 goes to fund agencies in the voluntary sector to provide services for drug misusers. Several of the projects in this category are supervised and managed by social work departments. In addition since 1988 all health boards have been given "earmarked" funding (distributed according to the normal allocation formula for hospital and community health provision) for the improvement and expansion of drug misuse services. This is known as GEN2 money under the terms of the NHS Circular which announced the allocation of resources. In 1993-94 health boards received some £2.47m under the GEN2 and GEN6 arrangements.

6.5   Moreover, since 1987 all health boards have received additional allocations to enable them to respond to the extra burdens created by HIV and AIDS. The close link between HIV/AIDS and drug misuse in Scotland has made it difficult to draw a clear demarcation line; and in recognition of this The Scottish Office has encouraged boards to use their AIDS allocations for drug-related initiatives, where these are demonstrably linked to HIV/AIDS. So, for example, needle exchanges have typically been funded from this source. In 1993/94 some £3.18m (out of total HIV/AIDS allocations of £19.4m) was spent on services related to drug misuse. This was in addition to the allocations under GEN2 and GEN6.

6.6   Following a review of these funding arrangements, allocations to health boards for drug services are now being made on the basis of service agreements drawn up by the National Services Division of the NHS and agreed with each board. For 1994-95 these service agreements have been drawn up on the basis of bids from the health boards for their HIV/AIDS and drug misuse services provision. In addition to allowing greater sensitivity to local needs - which was arguably missing from the GEN6 and GEN2 arrangements - the new service agreements separate out the drugs element from the HIV/AIDS allocations and provides the "transparency" in funding sought by the Scottish Affairs Committee in its report (paragraph 118). The Drugs Task Force welcomes these improved arrangements and the greater clarity now achieved in the purposes for which this funding is given to health boards.

6.7 Funding of local authority provision for community care services is channelled through the resources made available generally under revenue support grant; there is no earmarking of community care money although the sums have been clearly identified within Grant Aided Expenditure. Within the overall amount identified for community care expenditure, sums have also been nominally allocated to community care client groups. Central government support for drug misuse services is included within the "other community services" line in the grant aided expenditure settlement. It is known that certain local authorities also allocate resources to drug services from other main social work expenditure programmes - eg children and families, mental health. Given the variety of funding arrangements within local authorities and because resources for drug misuse are usually pooled with other resources for alcohol misuse it is difficult to determine a precise figure of total local authority expenditure on drug misuse. The Scottish Office Statistical Bulletin on local authority social work expenditure 1991-92 suggests expenditure on drugs services at that time could be estimated at £2.3m. Since then the expenditure on drug services by local authorities is likely to have risen significantly with the probability that some of the additional monies made available to local authorities to implement community care will have gone on drug services. It is clearly important for planning purposes to have at least indicative information on the level of local authority resources being devoted to services for drug misusers and their families. **We recommend that The Scottish Office should assess the usefulness of the information already provided by local authorities,and assess what additional information may be required on an annual basis,to provide a full picture of local authority expenditure on drug misuse services in Scotland.**

6.8 One of the fundamental issues in relation to funding which concerned the Drugs Task Force was whether funding for the provision of services should be earmarked or issued with general allocations. The only earmarked funding provided for drug misuse work is the funding given to health boards (as explained in paragraphs 6.4-6.6 above). Given that all other funding, police grant, funding for prisons etc is issued by way of general allocation the

Drugs Task Force considered whether there would be merit in moving in this direction in relation to health board funding. Its principal advantage would be in permitting health boards to take decisions about the allocation of resources for drug services against the competing claims of services provided for other patient groups. On the other hand, the requirement for a wide range of services for drug misusers is unlikely to diminish; indeed all the indications are that there should be an expansion of services. The maintenance of earmarked funding denotes the seriousness of the problem, and the national concern that effective action be taken. **Accordingly we recommend that earmarked funding to health boards for the provision of services for drug misusers - that is both drug services programmes and the drugs element of HIV/AIDS programmes - should continue for the foreseeable future.**

6.9 There are also strong arguments in favour of a degree of earmarking of local authority expenditure on drug misuse services in order to safeguard them. There are at present no powers available to the Secretary of State under which a specific grant for drug misuse services could be paid to local authorities. Although it is proposed, in the Local Government (Scotland) Bill, that the Secretary of State should have power, in exceptional circumstances, to pay a "special" grant to one or more local authorities, any approach involving the use of special or specific grant would run up against the presumption that local authorities should use their own discretion in setting funding priorities according to local circumstances. In these circumstances, we do not recommend the introduction of ring-fencing arrangements whereby a proportion of local authority expenditure, as determined by central government, would be reserved exclusively for drug misuse services. **There is however another, less constricting, option that merits consideration - setting an indicative spending level for local authority drug misuse services within grant aided expenditure. We recommend that The Scottish Office should explore this possibility.**

6.10 We have also considered whether to recommend a transfer of resources from health boards' drugs allocations to social work departments. At present, the health board funding of several voluntary sector projects is channelled through social work departments. These projects have a strong social care element and it is arguable that their funding should come from social work departments. There is also an argument of efficiency in favour of a transfer of resources, in that the current arrangements give risk to duplication in monitoring and project oversight. Looked at pragmatically, on the other hand, the present arrangements are well established, work adequately and enable earmarked resources available to health boards to be routed to desirable projects. Furthermore, we are conscious that social work expenditure is not ring-fenced. On balance, we conclude that no change should be made at present. The main priority must be to safeguard this important area of service provision and to ensure that the support given to projects is consistent with the broader inter-agency strategy. **However, given that there are examples elsewhere in the community care arena of resources being transferred from health boards to local authorities, we recommend that The Scottish Office should consider the scope for transferring the relevant funding to local authorities if a separate line is developed for drug misuse services within grant aided expenditure.**

6.11 It was brought to the attention of the Drugs Task Force that funding arrangements for the non-statutory sector often lack the security enjoyed by the statutory sector. We appreciate the uncertainty which this may engender in some service providers and **we recommend that, as far as possible, contracts with the non-statutory sector to provide drug misuse services should be drawn up to cover reasonable periods of time (say 3 to 4 years) to provide conditions of financial stability within which services can be developed.**

6.12 We share the concern of the Scottish Affairs Committee about the funding of drugs-related projects under the Urban Programme (paragraph 119 of the Committee's Report). The Urban Programme is an important instrument through which central government encourages local authorities to target expenditure on those urban areas suffering the most severe multiple deprivation. Support is offered, via local authorities, to a wide range of innovative projects intended to improve the social, economic and environmental conditions of residents of deprived areas. Projects can be run by a voluntary organisation, a community group or by a local authority itself. It appears that in a number of areas the existing local Drug Liaison Committees are not always aware that an application for a drug-related project has been lodged and have therefore had no opportunity to either consider or influence the thrust of the project. **We recommend that in future all applications for the funding of drugs-related projects under the Urban Programme should require to be endorsed by the area Drug Action Team; and that the DATs should play a proactive part in developing such**

proposals. Any other applications to The Scottish Office for funding of drug-related projects - for example under sections 9 and 10 of the Social Work (Scotland) Act 1968 - should similarly be approved by the Drug Action Teams.

7 CO-ORDINATION ARRANGEMENTS

7.1 In announcing the establishment of the Drugs Task Force, the Secretary of State stressed the importance of co-ordination, at both local and national level, in tackling the problem of drug misuse. Planning and co-ordination to ensure best utilisation of resources within an overall strategic plan are crucial. Clearly there are differences in the drugs situation across the country and it is important that services are organised on a local basis. Local agencies must take ownership of tackling the problem at local level. The contribution of the existing Drug Liaison Committees in bringing local agencies together has been significant but after some 6 years of operation it is right to consider whether the present arrangements can be improved. In paragraphs 7.2 to 7.14 we review the present arrangements and make proposals for more effective planning and co-ordination at local and national level.

LOCAL CO-ORDINATION

7.2 In 1987, The Scottish Office issued advice to health boards and local authorities on the development of local arrangements for monitoring the nature and extent of drug misuse in their areas and for co-ordinating action in the prevention of drug misuse and provision of treatment and rehabilitation services for drug misusers. The Scottish Office advised that there should be a Drug Liaison Committee (DLC) for each mainland local government region and, in the case of Strathclyde for each health board area in the region. Earlier reports by the ACMD which inter alia covered liaison and co-ordination suggested that the composition and method of working of these committees should be determined locally in the light of the local situation and the need to be able to respond to changing circumstances. Consequently, The Scottish Office did not specify precise arrangements, but suggested that the committees' membership should be drawn from all relevant agencies and professional disciplines.

7.3 Drug Liaison Committees have been established in all 15 health board areas in Scotland. In some they have been combined with Alcohol Misuse Co-ordinating Committees to form Addictions Liaison Committees. From the reports provided by DLCs to the Drugs Task Force it is clear that across the country a multi-agency approach has been adopted, the pattern of membership embracing health boards, local authority social work departments, education, the voluntary sector, police representatives, prisons and, in some areas, church and community groups. Generally, there appears to be a preponderance of health board representatives. The average size of DLCs ranges from the largest with 44 members to the smallest with 11 members. Reporting arrangements vary but in a number of areas the DLC is accountable to the Joint Planning Team (health board and regional council) while in other areas reporting lines are back to parent bodies. Most of the DLCs have developed strategic plans but it is not clear that the plan is "owned" by all the agencies represented. The picture is of DLCs across the country varying considerably in terms of structure, membership, planning and effectiveness.

7.4 Although some Drugs Liaison Committees have performed well, the Drugs Task Force has reached the conclusion that the time has come for a more focused and vigorous approach towards co-ordination of drug polices at local level. **Accordingly, we recommend that, in each health board area, a small group of senior people should be established to draw up an action plan for tackling drug misuse locally and thereafter driving and monitoring its delivery. This group - which we recommend should be known as the Drug Action Team - should consist of senior local figures from the statutory and non-statutory agencies, including the health board, the social work department, the education department, the police and the voluntary sector.** In addition to this core membership, Teams may include, by local decision, representatives of the prison service and the Scottish Drugs Forum, but in no case should a Team have more than 12 members.

7.5 The Drug Action Team will not have any executive powers. It will, however, draw together the key players who have the capacity to act on or influence the agencies at the forefront of tackling drug misuse.

Shaping a coherent overall drugs strategy for the area and sharpening the response to the complex issues surrounding drug misuse will be the DAT's raison d'etre. It will perform the key function of planning, co-ordinating and stimulating local action on drug misuse. Delivery of services will be a matter for the existing agencies, taking account of the plan drawn up by the Drug Action Team. Planning can seem dull but it is essential, particularly in dealing with a multi-faceted problem such as drug misuse, if local effort is to be targeted on greatest need, if overlaps and gaps are to be eliminated and if all the agencies which have parts to play are to sing the same tune. Moreover, we stress that by planning we do not envisage the simple amalgamation of descriptions of the ongoing work of the various agencies. We look to the Drug Action Teams to develop a broad strategic approach, based on their assessment of the extent and nature of the local problem, to bring forward imaginative proposals for proactive programmes and to challenge the perspectives and approaches of individual agencies where this is necessary.

7.6 If Drug Action Teams are to perform this role, they need to consist of senior people who are knowledgeable about the problem, able to contribute to the development of a broad perspective and able to carry the Drug Action Team's vision back to their individual agencies and secure its delivery. **We envisage that the Drug Action Team should consist of officers who are at, or just below, chief officer level.** The Chairman will have a vital role in bringing the Team together and ensuring that members play their full parts. He or she needs to be a person of seniority and weight locally. **We recommend that the Chairman should be of chief officer level - that is to say a Health Board General Manager, a Director of Social Work, a Director of Education, a Chief Constable or a person of similar standing.** We do not wish to prescribe that he or she should come from a particular agency since this is best settled locally and in any event we think that there would be advantage in having a diversity of chairmanship across Scotland. **Accordingly we recommend that the Chairman should be selected through the machinery which exists locally for consultation at chief officer level, following whatever wider consultation seems appropriate. We further recommend that the Chairman should report regularly to the local chief officers group on the activities of the Drug Action Team.**

7.7 The DAT's strategic plan will extend beyond the provision of services provided through the existing machinery for joint community care planning which brings together health boards and social work departments. While the value and importance of this joint planning in the provision of services is recognised by the Drugs Task Force, the complex nature of drug misuse demands a broader response if the problem is to be tackled effectively. Accordingly the DAT strategic plan will need to encompass the full range of policy issues impinging on drug misuse, including prevention and education, policing, service provision by social work departments and health boards, and the contribution of the voluntary sector. Where applicable, it will need to take account of any prisons dimension. In other words it requires to be an all-embracing strategic plan covering every aspect of drug misuse. The strategic plan drawn up by the Drug Action Teams and the drugs element within community care plans will therefore complement and inform each other. Given appropriately senior representation on the Drug Action Team we see no difficulty and much potential advantage in this cross-fertilisation.

7.8 **Drug Action Teams should be established in all health board areas by 1 April 1995. Within 6 months they should draw up strategic plans for tackling drug misuse in their areas. Although teams are to be locally based and not subject to central direction, we recommend that The Scottish Office should monitor their development, should receive and assess their strategic and annual operating plans and should use its good offices to resolve any difficulties which may arise locally.**

7.9 In recommending that Drug Action Teams should be based on health board areas, we are conscious that the forthcoming local government reorganisation will disrupt existing patterns of liaison between local authorities and health boards. Some health board areas will in future contain a number of local government units, each with their own social work and education departments. On the other hand police force and health board areas will in many cases continue to match. Our recommendation that Drug Action Teams should be based on health board areas takes account of the fact that we wish these teams to take a strategic view. We are keen to avoid the creation of too many Teams with too localised a view. We recognise, and accept, that this means that, following local government reorganisation, the social work departments and education departments in a health board area will need to develop machinery for agreeing representation on the Drug Action Team and for contributing to, and taking on board the outcome of, its work. An additional advantage of basing Teams on health board areas will be to keep an element of continuity and direction during the period when local government is in transition.

7.10   In the reports provided by DLCs to the Drugs Task Force there were suggestions for the appointment of Development Officers. This approach has been pioneered in the alcohol field; each of the Alcohol Misuse Co-ordinating Committees (AMCC) in Scotland has an Alcohol Development Officer. The value of this approach is still being assessed but the initial indications are that these appointments have been a helpful contribution to the effectiveness of the AMCCs. **The Drugs Task Force believes that it would be helpful in enabling the Drug Action Teams to develop and expand their work if The Scottish Office was to provide the necessary funding to enable each of these new Teams to be supported by a Drugs Development Officer (who might be full or part time depending on the extent of the local problem). We recommend accordingly** . The principal duty of the Drugs Development Officer (DDO) would be to ensure that all the component parts of the strategic plan were being carried out but other duties might include a role in prevalence work and needs assessments or mobilising community involvement in drugs issues. An important issue is where the DDO should be located organisationally. The arrangement which has operated with the Alcohol Development Officers is that they are placed with either the health board or the local authority depending on what is agreed locally. Similar arrangements seem appropriate in respect of Drugs Development Officers.

7.11   If Drug Action Teams are to be small, as we think essential, many agencies or interests doing work in the drug misuse field will not be able to be represented. (Indeed in many cases those currently represented on Drug Liaison Committees will not have seats on the new Teams.) **We recommend that, to support and inform the work of each DAT, a Drugs Forum, covering the same catchment area, should be established. This should be broadly based, representing the interests of those who provide services to drug misusers, drug misusers themselves and their families and carers, and representatives of communities affected by drug misuse. The main purpose of the Forum would be to ascertain, co-ordinate and express the views of service providers, service users and those in need of services.** Membership should be open to any responsible organisation with an interest and role in the field of drugs prevention or care of those affected by drug misuse including community action groups. This suggests, essentially, an open structure which can adapt to developing and changing patterns of organised response to drug misuse. The Forum should meet regularly and report to DATs and other local planning systems. It has the potential to be a very valuable source of information about community attitudes, feedback on services and ideas for local initiatives. The Scottish Office should issue guidance on the composition and work of these Drug Forums.

NATIONAL CO-ORDINATION

7.12 The Government's strategy for tackling drug misuse focuses action on 5 main fronts:–

1. international action - co-operating with other countries in efforts to curb the production, trafficking and misuse of drugs;

2. making enforcement even more effective - enhancing Customs and police enforcement of the laws against trafficking and misuse of drugs;

3. maintaining effective deterrents and tight domestic controls - deterring drug dealers by high maximum penalties and by depriving them of the proceeds of their crimes and operating tight controls on drugs prescribed for medicinal uses in order to minimise leakage to the illicit market;

4. developing prevention - discouraging those who are not misusing drugs from doing so and those who misuse drugs occasionally from progressing to more regular misuse;

5. improving treatment and rehabilitation - helping those who are already misusing to stop doing so, and, where this cannot be done immediately, to reduce the harm they do to themselves and others.

The Scottish Office plays its full part at UK level in debating, discussing and developing policies to tackle drug misuse within this general strategy. The Minister of State at The Scottish Office - the Chairman of the Task Force - is a member of the Ministerial Committee which keeps the strategy under review and co-ordinates policy to tackle drug misuse throughout the United Kingdom. While the strategy provides the foundation for policy and operational planning, within the four home countries of Scotland, England, Wales and Northern Ireland, the scale and nature of the problem differs and the response adopted has to reflect these differences.

7.13 In Scotland policy on the various aspects of drug misuse has been co-ordinated by a multi-disciplinary group of officials in The Scottish Office - the Working Group on Drug Misuse. In addition The Scottish Office has regular meetings with health board Drug Misuse Co-ordinators. These meetings have provided a focus for useful exchanges of information and views and for discussion of major issues of concern in the health field. However, the Drugs Task Force shares the concern of the Scottish Affairs Committee (paragraph 111 of its report) that there is at present no national forum in Scotlandfor bringing together all those involved in the field to plan a coherent strategy for Scotland and to co-ordinate action. We believe that steps should be taken as a matter of priority to establish such a forum.

7.14 The Drugs Task Force considers that a new national committee should be established to advise Government and inform policy. It should have a Scotland wide remit to gather information, analyse and provide advice. The core membership of this national committee would include authoritative figures in the drug misuse field in Scotland, the Scottish members of the ACMD, those working in research and training and others with recognised expertise and experience in the drugs field. The committee would focus on specific Scottish themes, and would undertake or commission work on topics of particular concern or specific relevance in Scotland. It would also provide a forum for the dissemination of best practice and the development of new thinking. **Accordingly, we recommend that The Scottish Office should establish a Scottish advisory committee on drug misuse, reporting to the Secretary of State for Scotland, to provide advice on policy, priorities and strategic planning.** The strategic plans drawn up by each Drug Action Team will be informed by the outcome of the work of the Scottish advisory committee on drug misuse and will in turn assist the work of the committee. This flow of information between The Scottish Office (which will be assessing the work of the DATs), the Scottish advisory committee on drug misuse (which will be advising the Secretary of State on policy and priorities) and the DATs (who will be tackling drug misuse at local level) should ensure that all concerned are working within a coherent framework.

A NATIONAL STRATEGY FOR TRAINING

7.15 The consequences of drug misuse have implications for a wide range of professional and voluntary workers in the statutory and voluntary sectors. This in turn creates a need for good training to equip those involved with the skills and expertise to deal with the myriad problems with which they are confronted. For some staff this may involve a basic level of awareness and understanding of the drug misuse problem so that they can recognise when a problem is drug-related; for others a more advanced level of training is required to give them specific skills in dealing with drug misusers; and at a higher level there is a need for specialist training to enable those concerned to provide an effective service in managing drug-related problems. **In essence there is a need for adequate, relevant and continuing training to ensure that all those staff whose work impacts directly or indirectly on the drug misuse scene can maximise their effectiveness in dealing with the issues involved.** ACMD underscored the importance of training in its 1990 Report which was brought to the attention of the training and validating bodies of a number of the professions concerned in Scotland.

7.16 A basic level of training in drug misuse issues is given by a number of the professions, including the medical, pharmaceutical, nursing, social work and teaching professions, at both the pre and post qualifying stages. Training in drug misuse issues is also given to police and prison officers. This is complemented by the specialist and advanced training carried out at the Drugs Training Project (DTP) at Stirling University and the Centre for Alcohol and Drug Studies (CADS) at Paisley University, both of which receive Scottish Office funding. In addition the Health Education Board for Scotland, the Scottish Drugs Forum and the Scottish AIDS Monitor, all of whom receive Scottish Office funding, also make a contribution in the training field.

7.17 However, in acknowledging the importance which the Government attaches to ensuring that training provision reflects service needs, The Scottish Office issued a consultation document entitled "Towards A National Strategy For Substance Misuse Training in Scotland" in November 1993. The consultation document, in Part I, set out proposals for securing greater cohesion and integration in the work of DTP and CADS; and in Part II set out a number of aims and objectives around which a strategy for substance misuse training might be developed. The Scottish Office has been analysing the large number of responses received with a view to determining how the issues concerned might be taken forward. The Drugs Task Force welcomes the issue of this consultation document as an important first step in determining a strategy which will embrace the training needs of all those working in the drug misuse field. **We recommend that the development of a strategy for drug misuse training in Scotland should now be taken forward by the Scottish advisory committee (referred to in paragraph 7.14 above).** In the meantime discussions should take place between The Scottish Office, the DTP and CADS to determine the most appropriate arrangements for the future activities of these 2 training bodies.

7.18 Training and education in the drugs field also need to address the specific difficulties and needs of women drug misusers. Agencies should ensure that their staff are aware, and have an understanding, of the particular issues relating to women.

8 THE ROLE OF THE CRIMINAL JUSTICE AGENCIES

8.1 The misuse of controlled drugs is an illegal activity - albeit with important social and medical connotations. In this chapter we address the role of the criminal justice agencies in dealing with drug misuse.

THE POLICE

8.2 The police clearly have a crucial role in tackling drug misuse. Elsewhere in this report we have emphasised their important contribution in the prevention field, both in schools and in the community at large. Their primary activity in relation to drug misuse is, however, detection and enforcement. In addition to pursuing drugs offences, police forces in Scotland have accorded a high priority to targeting those who supply and deal in drugs. Career criminals are undoubtedly responsible for major drug trafficking since the profit margin from drug dealing is huge in comparison to almost all other forms of criminal activity. The police strategy in tackling drug misuse follows the recommendations of the Broome Report (1985) and is organised on 3 broad levels, respectively directed at major traffickers, middle-level dealers and small-time dealers/users. The Scottish Crime Squad, which operates throughout Scotland, is responsible for identifying and directing operations against the major traffickers who operate across police force, and even national, boundaries. The middle-level dealers are targeted within force boundaries by the Drug Squads of the individual forces concerned. Street level dealers may also be targeted by force Drug Squads but, in the larger forces in particular, might also be handled at Divisional level.

8.3　In Scotland in 1981, 1,626 drug offences were recorded by the police. By 1993, this had risen to 17,986 offences, an increase of over 1,100%. This increase reflects not only the scale of drug misuse but the improved management of effort by the police in tackling the problem. By far the largest number of drug offences recorded relate to cannabis. This does not mean that the police give any greater priority to cannabis but simply reflects the pattern of misuse which they uncover in their investigations.

8.4　It is sometimes argued that the police would be better to concentrate their efforts on "hard" drugs such as cocaine and heroin and less time in pursuit of those who deal in "soft" drugs such as cannabis. The reality is that the major dealers do not draw any distinction between "hard" and "soft" drugs and will deal in any substance that provides them with a profit. There are plenty of examples of the police targeting drugs traffickers in the expectation of netting a particular drug such as cannabis and unexpectedly seizing heroin or another "hard" drug. Rightly, in our opinion, the police take the view that they cannot sensibly or practically make distinctions between drugs in their operations directed at major dealers. The Drugs Task Force has considered the Thematic Inspection Report on The Misuse of Drugs prepared by Her Majesty's Inspectorate of Constabulary. This is a very detailed report covering all aspects of police work in respect of the arrangements developed by the police to ensure an effective response to the problem of drug misuse and we endorse its recommendations.

8.5　There is no doubt that drug misusers commit crime to fund their habit. Acquisitive crimes such as housebreaking, shoplifting, cheque and credit card fraud go hand in hand with drug misuse. Scottish police forces do not routinely collect statistics on drug related crime and are not convinced that to do so would contribute significantly. However, the Scottish Affairs Committee is of the view (paragraph 171 of its Report) that a mechanism should be devised whereby drug-related crimes are recorded. On this, we note that reliable statistics would be difficult to obtain and could in practice only relate to detected crime. Where the offender is not identified it will be rarely, if ever, possible to be sure about his or her motives. Furthermore, where an offender is identified, information about his or her motives may be unreliable since many offenders are likely to misrepresent their situation particularly where they see advantage by way of, for example, non-prosecution or prosecution on a lesser charge. Any attempt to obtain reliable statistics would have to be pursued post-prosecution, although the reliability factor would still be questionable. We are therefore very doubtful whether a new system of recording drug-related crime on the lines suggested by the Scottish Affairs Committee would justify its costs. However we recognise that useful information may be obtained through specific research studies.

8.6 Rather than investing a lot of effort in constructing a recording system which may not in practice produce reliable results, we consider that priority should be given directly to the identification and development of measures to reduce the level of drug related crimes. This is clearly difficult but there is some research evidence (Report by Ms Sally Haw: Pharmaceutical Drugs and Illicit Drug Use in Lothian Region) that substitute prescribing under the auspices of the Lothian Community Drug Problem Service has had an influence on the criminal behaviour of drug misusers. **A similar study of criminal behaviour of drug misusers following the establishment of the Glasgow Drug Problem Service would clearly be of interest in determining the extent to which the evidence from the Lothian study is borne out. We recommend that such a study should be carried out.**

8.7 The police will be key members of the Drug Action Teams recommended in Chapter 7. This reflects not only the importance of their enforcement and prevention role but also the generally constructive relations which currently exist between the police and the other agencies working in the drugs field. This constructive dialogue can be built on and enhanced through the police contribution to the DAT structure. Developing and maintaining good relations between the police and local drug services will be helpful, including, for example, to police surgeons who have responsibility for the care of drug misusers in police custody. Police stations should also ensure that they have a stock of drug education and reference materials and know how to refer misusers to drug services. In Scotland a number of police forces have introduced "drug referral" cards which are designed to put people with drug problems in touch with services.

DRUG PROFIT CONFISCATION

8.8 Confiscation of the proceeds of drugs trafficking has been available to the High Court in Scotland since 1988, under the Criminal Justice

(Scotland) Act 1987. It is not available in Sheriff Court cases (except where the Sheriff remits to the High Court for sentence) and it is discretionary on both the prosecutor and the court. There are also complex issues relating to the making of a confiscation order. The most significant practical deficiency in the existing legislation is the exclusion of Sheriff Court cases which constitute a significant proportion of drug trafficking prosecutions. The police and the Crown Office are of the view that if confiscation was available in the Sheriff Court they would certainly be able to report and deal with more cases where there was evidence of identifiable assets and unexplained income. In England and Wales, under the Drug Trafficking Offences Act 1986 confiscation is mandatory on conviction for a trafficking offence (although a degree of discretion is to be introduced by the Criminal Justice Act 1993). The result is that a large number of very small confiscation orders have been made. The average confiscation order in England and Wales in 1993 was about £7,500 whereas by contrast the average confiscation order in Scotland during the same period was about £69,000. Although the discretionary element has undoubtedly resulted in a much smaller number of confiscation orders being made in Scotland than in England and Wales there remains a significant disparity in the overall value of confiscation - £62m in England and Wales and £400,000 in Scotland. The recently published report by the Scottish Law Commission on its examination of criminal forfeiture and confiscation suggests the extension of confiscation orders to the Sheriff Courts as well as other extensions to the confiscation regime. **We attach the greatest importance to reducing the profitability of drug trafficking and we welcome the Scottish Law Commission's proposal to enable the Sheriff Courts to make drug profit confiscation orders.** We note that the Government has now announced its intention in the White Paper "Firm and Fair" (Cm 2600) to bring forward legislative proposals at the earliest opportunity, following consideration of the Scottish Law Commission's recommendations.

8.9 Responsibility for operating the drug profit confiscation procedures falls largely upon the Crown Office and despite the smaller number of cases brought to court, considerable police and prosecution resources have been committed to drug profit confiscation work. A number of police forces have set up dedicated financial investigation units, and the Scottish Crime Squad has assigned an officer with responsibility for drugs profit confiscation work to each of its 5 syndicates. Specialist advice is provided by the Crown Office Fraud and Specialist Services Unit. The small number of cases dealt with has enabled the police and the Crown Office to concentrate resources on carrying out the most detailed financial profile on the accused and extensive investigation of their assets. This has led to confiscation being ordered in every case where it was moved for by the prosecutor. **The Drugs Task Force vigorously endorses the efforts being put into pursuing drug profit confiscation by the police and prosecution authorities.**

DIVERSION SCHEMES

8.10 It is a criminal offence to possess or supply controlled drugs. The criminal justice system needs to be capable of dealing with a range of circumstances, and a range of individuals accused of drug related offending. At one end of the spectrum major dealers or suppliers of drugs are dealt with in the High Court and can expect to receive, on conviction, very heavy sentences. In 1994 a convicted drug trafficker was sentenced to 30 years and the maximum sentence is life imprisonment. At the other end, young people are experimenting with illicit drugs and, especially in socially deprived areas, are at risk of being sucked into the drug scene and crime. In addition, there are the small scale traffickers, very often drug misusers themselves, who are involved in low level dealing simply to support their drug habit but who are not yet committing other crimes to support that habit. These individuals are all links in the drug trafficking chain. Some will require to be dealt with by the full weight of the criminal law; for others, the best way to break any growing dependency on drugs and therefore serve the public interest may be to find alternatives to prosecution.

8.11 In drugs cases, as with all other cases, the Procurator Fiscal must decide the appropriate course of action to take in the public interest. Parliament has taken a serious view of drug misuse by providing heavy penalties for those convicted of drugs offences. The highest penalties relate to trafficking and dealing, and such cases are likely to be prosecuted in the High Court or the Sheriff Court. Penalties for possession are graded according to the class of drug involved. However, even the "simple possession" of a Class B drug such as cannabis can attract a maximum of 5 years imprisonment. The Drugs Task Force understands that in reaching a decision about a particular drugs case, the Procurator Fiscal will have regard to factors such as the class of controlled drug involved, the conduct of the accused, whether it is the accused's first offence and the circumstances of the alleged offence. In minor cases the Procurator Fiscal may decide that it would be more appropriate to give a warning to a particular individual, in which event the case will not come to court. In 1992-93, warning letters in simple possession cases were issued to 643 individuals representing 10% of simple possession reports received. Alternatively, if the Procurator Fiscal refers the individual for social work or psychiatric help instead of going ahead with the prosecution, the case may not come to court if that individual co-operates. The intention is to divert from prosecution accused persons who will benefit from diversion and who would otherwise have been prosecuted; the objective is to reduce the harm caused to the individual and the community. The purpose of such diversion schemes is, therefore, to prevent a recurrence of the alleged criminal behaviour, not to legitimise it.

8.12   It appears to the Drugs Task Force that the more options that Procurators Fiscal have at their disposal, the greater is the scope for the exercise of their discretion in the public interest. This approach has the advantage of encouraging more early self-disclosure of drug use, reducing recruitment into the drug sub-culture and keeping intervention by the criminal justice system and helping agencies in the community to the minimum necessary. We understand that at present in Scotland an offence relating to a Class A drug would normally lead automatically to prosecution. However, the Drugs Task Force's view is that the class of drug involved should not be a determining factor in ruling out the option of diversion. **We consider that decisions on diversion from prosecution should be made on the basis of the circumstances of the individual drug misuser and the alleged offence as well as the substance concerned, and recommend that the Lord Advocate considers this approach in any guidance he issues to Procurators Fiscal in connection with diversion.**

8.13   Formal schemes for diversion from prosecution to social work exist in a number of areas. At present 7 local authority run schemes are operating in Scottish courts: in Grampian, Highland, Lothians (2 schemes), Strathclyde and Tayside Regions and the Orkney Isles. In addition, there are 2 formal psychiatric diversion facilities, in Glasgow and Inverness, and SACRO (formerly the Scottish Association for the Care and Rehabilitation of Offenders) runs several reparation and mediation schemes linked to diversion. The number of alleged offenders currently subject to formal diversion from prosecution across the range of all cases (not just drugs) is small - 1000 out of 170,000 charged over the period March 1992 to February 1993. Social work schemes are almost entirely funded by local authorities because, although they are seen as essential components of a comprehensive social work service in the criminal justice system, it has not proved possible until now to include them within the scope of 100% funding arrangements by the Social Work Services Group of The Scottish Office for these services.

8.14 The potential of social work diversion schemes for reducing harm to the individual and the community could be considerable but has not yet been fully tested. SWSG is developing a range of diversion options for objective assessment and evaluation before decisions are taken on future policy. A small number of pilot schemes will be established, with direct funding from SWSG, to evaluate their costs and benefits. It is envisaged that services for drug misusers could form a component of at least some of the pilot schemes. The Drugs Task Force recognises the value of such schemes for diverting alleged offenders from prosecution. In suitable cases, diversion can be more effective in changing the behaviour of selected individuals. **We welcome the decision by SWSG to establish a number of pilot schemes and recommend that sufficient provision for alleged offenders with drug related problems is included in these schemes to enable future policy and funding decisions to be made in the light of practical experience.**

8.15 The present range of diversion schemes tend to offer group work or individual counselling and there is clearly a need to explore a wider range and variety of programmes based on the needs of the individuals selected as suitable for this form of disposal. This might embrace short, user friendly, learning programmes focused on the dangers of drug use to personal health, personal and social functioning, risk of involvement in crime and punishment, including the acquisition of avoidance techniques and other social skills. Consideration could be given to involving ex-users as trainers and motivators to improve access to and credibility of these programmes as well as providing an opportunity for ex-users to use their experiences constructively. The potential contribution of the voluntary sector in the provision of diversion schemes and particularly in terms of their ability to provide a range of different options should also be explored. Such schemes could also be expected to improve access to health care services in appropriate areas.

8.16   The public rightly take a serious view of drug misuse and there can be no question of any "easy options" - in the form of diversion - being introduced for alleged drugs offenders. Indeed diversion is not a substitute for existing forms of disposal by the Procurator Fiscal, rather an addition to the range. The discretion to use the decision to divert must rest with the Procurator Fiscal but be based on reports from the police and the social services which contain relevant and adequate information so that a decision on diversion can be made with confidence that it is appropriate in the circumstances. Furthermore, the Procurator Fiscal may use one or both of 2 procedures for diversion; either to waive prosecution altogether or defer prosecution pending the outcome of the proposed intervention and retain the right to prosecute. It is for the Procurator Fiscal, in consultation with social work departments, to decide which of these options should be included in the working arrangements for such schemes. The nature of the diversion from prosecution approach suggests that it has the potential to be most beneficial for the younger age group where early intervention might avoid criminalisation and divert young people from a drug misusing path. In due course, there may be scope for extending its use to long-term drug misusers who are seriously trying to overcome their dependency and associated problems but who relapse, as an incentive to maintain their efforts. **We endorse the use of diversion and recommend that Drug Action Teams address, in consultation with Procurators Fiscal, the development of diversion schemes in their area within the context of their strategic plans.**

ALTERNATIVES TO CUSTODY

8.17   In Part I of its report on "Drug Misusers and the Criminal Justice System" (1991), the Advisory Council on the Misuse of Drugs argued *"that community sentences are likely to be a more effective way than prison of dealing with less serious drug misusing offenders, in terms of the protection of the public, the prevention of re-offending and the successful re-integration of the offender in the community. Our enquiries have confirmed us in the view that increased use of community penalties for drug misusers is essential if these objectives are to be achieved. The aim behind community penalties will be to impose a sanction which makes serious demands on the offender and offers a reasonable prospect of preventing further offending at least as effectively as a prison sentence would...."* (paragraph 2.8). The Drugs Task Force endorses this view and wishes to emphasise the crucial contribution which co-ordinated effort by social work and health care agencies can make towards increasing the provision of credible and realistic programmes, linked to supervision in the community, for consideration by sentencers instead of custody.

8.18 Where an offender is convicted of a drug related offence, the court faces a similar difficulty to that facing the Procurator Fiscal in identifying the most appropriate disposal in the circumstances of the case. The court's options include admonition, a financial penalty, probation, community service and custody. In reaching its decision, the court needs reliable information about those aspects of the offender's circumstances and behaviour which have a bearing on his or her offending, including that relating to drug misuse; and the availability of community-based sanctions which will help reduce the risk of further offending and assist the offender's integration in the community.

8.19 One of the main sources of such information and advice is the social enquiry report prepared by social work departments. Courts are required to obtain such reports before imposing either a first sentence of imprisonment on an offender aged 21 or over, or any sentence of detention on an offender between the age of 16 and 20. The national standards for the preparation of these reports, issued by The Scottish Office, already stress the need to be alert to the possibility that the offending behaviour may be drug related (paragraphs 37.5 and 47.5.1); to be familiar with the range of available services and programmes which might be used in association with a community-based disposal (paragraph 58); and to consult with specialist services in support of any action plan which might be presented to the court for consideration, taking into account the views of the social work department, other statutory and voluntary agencies and medical practitioners (paragraphs 57 and 59).

8.20 Social enquiry reports are therefore a crucial link between the court and the services made available by local authorities and other agencies to deal with the offender in the community. Local authorities' responsibilities for social work criminal justice services require them to take a pivotal role in developing - for drug misusing offenders as for others - integrated social work and health care services linked to criminal justice sanctions. The Drugs Task Force is aware of the significant steps which some local authorities are already taking to develop programmes linked to probation supervision which can be offered in social enquiry reports and used by the courts instead of custody. **We consider there is scope for greater use of such programmes, especially in more rural areas. We recommend that local authorities address these issues in the context of their 3 year strategic plans for offender services and the annual updates. In line with earlier comments on the voluntary sector, drug agencies will need to consider how they can provide a service linked to criminal justice disposals, which involve a measure of compulsion and which require enforcement for non-compliance, alongside services provided on a voluntary basis.**

8.21　The Drugs Task Force welcomes the recent establishment of earmarked funding within the 100% funding arrangements to assist the development of pilot programmes specifically designed to help offenders with alcohol and/or drug misuse problems. It also welcomes the recent grant awarded to the Scottish Drugs Forum to appoint a development officer who will identify service gaps and assist in the development of services for illicit drug users especially those at risk of a custodial sentence. Taken together, these 2 initiatives provide a useful framework for further service improvements. The Drugs Task Force also welcomes the recent inclusion of bail services within the framework of 100% funding as a significant contribution to the overall network of services. In due course, it is hoped that social work departments will be in a position to include services for drug misusers as part of their wider development of bail information and bail supervision services, following evaluation of current pilots.

8.22　The recent Government White Paper on "Scotland's Children" drew attention to the existence of a small group of vulnerable young offenders between the ages of 16 and 18 for whom prosecution might not be appropriate because of their immaturity. Some of these young offenders may be experimenting with illicit drugs and drifting further into crime to support their habit. The Drugs Task Force supports the view that programmes of care and supervision under existing powers through the Children's Hearing System may be a more effective way of helping these young people address their offending and the harm caused by their drug use. However, proposals to the courts in social enquiry reports to remit such cases to the Children's Hearing for advice on disposal cannot realistically be made unless suitable programmes are available. **We recommend that local authorities examine how best use can be made of existing resources and what**

programmes may need to be developed to enable these young offenders to be dealt with by the Children's Hearings. This should form part of the wider strategy developed by local authorities for helping children in care who are experiencing problems related to drug misuse (as referred to in paragraph 3.31).

8.23   Many drug misusing offenders live fairly chaotic lives. They may not have the means to pay a financial penalty nor the capacity to cope with the demands of a community service order. They are likely to face serious and complex problems and require access to both health and social services. Relapse is a frequent occurrence; and services and sentencing need to take account of this. A range of services is needed which are adapted to the circumstances of individual offenders, including residential and day programmes and multi-disciplinary approaches. While programmes which demand total abstinence may be suitable for some they will be unsuitable for others. Substitute prescribing may therefore provide a more realistic approach in some cases. It is more likely to motivate offenders to accept services, provides an important means of stabilising their lifestyle and reduces the risk of breach. However, if the problem of relapse is to be dealt with realistically, programme development will require not just close co-operation with health services and voluntary sector agencies but also close consultation with the judiciary. **We recommend that local authorities and health boards should examine the scope for incorporating substitute prescribing in programmes for drug misusing offenders linked to probation and other appropriate disposals.** Any such proposals should be discussed in advance with the local judiciary.

8.24   While individual needs may differ, most drug misusers who are dealt with in the criminal justice system are likely to need combinations of similar health and social care services, whether they are being dealt with in the context of prosecution, sentencing or release from custody. Equally, decision-makers at each stage in the criminal justice process require speedy and straightforward referral procedures for the purposes of assessment and advice about what services might be used in support of decisions relating to diversion from prosecution, the use of bail, community-based sanctions and parole licence. Local authorities are responsible for providing social work services in the criminal justice system and for aligning these services with social work services generally in the community - notably those for community care and children. They are therefore well placed to stimulate the development of systems for joint planning, management and service delivery by all the agencies which have a contribution to make to providing services in the community for drug misusers in trouble with the law. Resources are scarce. They therefore have to be accessible to those who need them, deployed flexibly, and used as efficiently as possible. **We therefore recommend that The Scottish Office should explore the feasibility of a single entry system to assessment for, and access to, community social and health care services which might be used to assist decision-making at each stage in the criminal justice process.**

THE SCOTTISH PRISON SERVICE

8.25 The prison service is a particular focus of attention in the context of drug misuse. Firstly, because the prison population includes a substantial number of individuals who have been convicted of drug offences, both possession and supply. Secondly, because the prison population includes a substantial number of drug misusers, some but not all of whom have been convicted of drug-related offences, whose drug misuse requires to be tackled during their period in custody. Thirdly, because we know that within prisons drug misuse activity takes place and presents particular problems of detection and control for prison staff.

8.26 The main task of the Scottish Prison Service is to keep in custody those committed by the courts, to maintain good order in each prison, to care for prisoners with humanity and to provide prisoners with a range of opportunities to exercise personal responsibility and to prepare for release. In 1991, 403 (10%) of all persons in Scotland found guilty of drugs offences were sentenced to a period of custody. In early 1993 the average number of such offenders was 370, which was 6.5% of the daily prisoner population. Of this group the majority, 222 (55%) were sentenced for offences solely related to cannabis. Not all of this group will themselves be drug misusers. The highest number of drug misusers are in fact those sentenced for other offences. These prisoners cover the range of drug misusing behaviour from occasional use to those who are persistent drug misusers and who may or may not be under treatment in the community (eg by substitute prescribing). Numbers are, however, difficult to estimate and depend on self-disclosure at or following admission to prison, or as a result of medical examination and interview. A survey of establishments in March 1993 indicated that from a population of some 5,900 prisoners 650 prisoners were injecting users prior to imprisonment. A period in prison provides an opportunity and a challenge for both the persistent drug misuser and for the prison service. The opportunity is to confront the drug misusing behaviour in a controlled environment with an effective treatment regime; the challenge is to return the prisoner back to the community in a drug-free state and to link him to support services in his locality.

8.27 Prisons in Scotland are expected to follow a common approach in dealing with the problem of drugs. Efforts are made to identify prisoners who misuse drugs at the medical examination given to all prisoners on admission. The medical response, if any, depends on the condition of the prisoner but should include medication to deal with the physical symptoms of withdrawal. More broadly, the Scottish Prison Service has recently adopted the policy that when a prisoner on a substitute prescribing maintenance programme is received into prison on a very short sentence or remand, the prison medical officer should consider whether such a programme should continue. This decision is to be taken in the light of the views of the prisoner and those of the doctor responsible for prescribing for the prisoner in the community. We welcome this decision. For very short-term prisoners it makes no sense to disrupt a treatment programme on which the prisoner was engaged before his entry to prison and to which he is likely to return on release.

8.28 The Drugs Task Force is encouraged by the pilot drug reduction programme being undertaken in Saughton Prison, Edinburgh involving the prescribing of drugs to participating prisoners over a period of 28 days on a reducing basis, combined with counselling and education. This programme is conducted within the prison hospital setting initially but with the prisoner being re-integrated into the prison regime over a period of 2-4 weeks. This is a very worthwhile initiative and in the light of the very positive outcome of the evaluation undertaken of the programme we would endorse the extension of this type of approach to other prisons. A similar approach has already been adopted at Glenochil and at Perth prisons. The Drugs Task Force is also encouraged by other projects involving counselling, information and education which are presently being carried out in Barlinnie and Low Moss. The importance of developing drug intervention, education and other programmes within the prison estate cannot be overemphasised.

8.29　In a recently produced guidance document prepared by the Scottish Prison Service and distributed to prison staff there is an exhortation that as far as possible drug programmes in prison should reflect the range of programmes available in the community. If this objective is to be met there is a need to address the question of drug treatment programmes in all prisons for longer-term prisoners. This is not to suggest open-ended maintenance but the need for a pragmatic approach for those prisoners for whom short period reduction programmes would be both inappropriate and unlikely to succeed. **We recommend that the Scottish Prison Service should further develop reduction to abstinence and education programmes for longer-term prisoners appropriate to the needs of the individuals.**

8.30　The Scottish Prison Service puts a high emphasis on having security measures in place to prevent, as far as possible, the presence of illegal drugs and their concomitant misuse in prisons. However, despite tight security measures, illegal drugs do find their way into the prison environment. The key to successful exclusion lies in a balance between security measures and programmes designed to reduce the demand for drugs in prison. Notwithstanding the measures which are in place a very small minority of prisoners, regrettably, engage in risky drug-taking behaviour, including the sharing of injecting equipment. There can be no question of condoning illegal drug taking in prison and for that reason, and because of the practical difficulties involved, needle exchanges are not acceptable. The emphasis is on providing prisoners with practical advice on drug-free lifestyles and harm minimisation. However in recognising that drug injecting and the sharing of needles does take place, the Drugs Task Force was involved in the decision, as part of a wider hygiene initiative, to make sterilising tablets available to all prisoners and, as a further pragmatic response, to provide guidance on how the tablets can be used to help sterilise injecting equipment. To be successful in addressing its aim it will be important for the prison authorities to continue to make sterilising tablets widely and discreetly available in easily accessible locations. Harm reduction strategies are an important part of tackling the drugs problem and should be kept under review by the Scottish Prison Service.

8.31　The risk of spreading HIV infection and other infections such as Hepatitis B, C and D from the sharing of needles is considerable. When this activity takes place in prisons the risks of spreading the infection is not just confined to the prison population but to the wider community when an infected prisoner is released. Following an outbreak of Hepatitis B in Glenochil in June 1993, 10 prisoners sought HIV blood tests and 8 were found to be HIV positive. In view of this all 372 adult prisoners were offered individual advice and counselling and an opportunity to be tested for HIV by independent counsellors. **It is imperative that the lessons from the HIV outbreak in Glenochil are learned and that the Scottish Prison Service takes practical pragmatic steps to eliminate, as far as possible, the risks of similar outbreaks in other establishments.** It will be important to ensure that the momentum generated following the Glenochil outbreak is maintained in order to establish a cadre of expertise in dealing with the drug misuse problem in Scottish prisons. In particular, it is essential that prison medical officers and associated staff are given adequate training both in recognising drug misuse symptoms and the range of measures available to respond to them. **We accordingly recommend that the Medical Adviser to the Scottish Prison Service should make arrangements for all prison medical staff to have regular training sessions on drug misuse issues, either inhouse or by attendance at external courses.** Six prison nursing staff from Glenochil are being trained at Ruchill Hospital on a pilot basis and this is a welcome development.

8.32   The Drugs Task Force welcomes the commitment which the Scottish Prison Service has to the throughcare of drug misusing prisoners and their families working with social work departments and specialist drug services in the community. Prisoners with drug related problems are already a high priority for prison-based social work units and most of these units already provide individual or group programmes for these prisoners. We welcome the recent joint initiative by Strathclyde and Central Regions to help women with drug related problems in HM Prison Cornton Vale to prepare for release and continue the programme on their return to Strathclyde Region. We also commend the programme which was recently developed by the Social Work Unit at HM Prison Saughton: this involves a specialist drug worker based in the Unit liaising with the pilot drug reduction programme in the prison, and specialist drug services in the community, to help prisoners prepare for release and working with the prisoner for a short period following his return to the community. Importantly, this worker is a member of the multi-disciplinary team in the prison which manages programmes for prisoners with drug problems.

8.33   Even for those prisoners who have successfully remained drug free while in prison, the temptation to return to their drug misusing ways on release in an environment where drugs might be readily available is likely to be extremely difficult to resist. Accordingly, the Drugs Task Force endorses the value of encouraging prisoners to seek the support of community-based agencies during their prison sentence and following their return to the community, as part of a continuous programme of throughcare. We believe that more could be done by prison-based staff in this regard. We also consider that more could be done to engage the partners and family members in throughcare programmes. Some partners or family members may themselves require assistance with a drug problem if any programme to help the prisoner is to succeed.

8.34 Providing effective throughcare programmes is a complex and difficult task. The Drugs Task Force considers it essential that a national framework of service objectives, priorities and standards for the throughcare of prisoners with drug problems and their families is developed as a basis for local joint initiatives by individual establishments, local authorities and other providers. The current Scottish Prison Service Drugs Strategy and the National Standards for Throughcare Services, presently under review, should provide a sound platform for the development of this framework. Funding implications may need to be considered to ensure that the families of prisoners have their proper place within the strategy bearing in mind that social work services for this group fall outwith the scope of the 100% funding arrangements. To ensure a co-ordinated approach to service development, consultation with key health and social care providers, as well as representatives of the different disciplines within prisons, will be necessary. **We therefore recommend that SWSG and the Scottish Prison Service should consider the feasibility of a throughcare pilot scheme to determine what combination of support and advice for prisoners with drug problems (and their families), during imprisonment and following return to the community, might help the prisoner to remain drug free on release and assist the development of good practice.**

8.35 The Scottish Drugs Forum has established a group to develop liaison between Tayside institutions which comprise HMP Perth, HMP Friarton, HMYOI Castle Huntly, HMP Noranside and the community-based drug services in Tayside. The group has proved effective in improving the working relationship between prison-based workers and those in the community and has led to practical improvements in the throughcare and discharge of prisoners with drug problems, in particular encouraging community-based agencies to develop work within the prison. The group aims to achieve consistency between institutions in terms of standards of practice and accuracy of materials used in all drug related work. **We support this initiative and urge Drug Action Teams to encourage similar arrangements in their areas which should lead to a consistent and equitable approach irrespective of what prison holds the prisoner. It may be necessary to co-ordinate and support these local initiatives. We recommend that the Scottish Prison Service and SWSG should consider how best this can be taken forward.**

8.36　In general the Drugs Task Force commends the many recent initiatives taken by the Scottish Prison Service to address the problem of drug misuse. **These initiatives now need to be developed and consolidated as general practice throughout the Scottish Prison Service so that the same services are available to drug misusing prisoners throughout Scotland.** In that connection, we welcome the issue of the Guidance Manual addressing the management of drug misuse and drug misusing prisoners as guidelines for all Scottish prisons to adopt and implement. Drug misuse is a fact of life in prisons as it is in the wider community. Encouraging prisoners with drug misuse problems to come forward in order to bring their drug problem into the open and seek help is the first step. Having taken this step it is essential that treatment and care programmes which meet the needs of prisoners are available. These programmes should be aimed at setting prisoners on the road to recovery or, at least, reducing the risk from their covert drug misuse. As far as possible the range of service provision for drug misusers in prison should mirror best practice in the wider community and should extend across the whole prison estate in Scotland. Furthermore these programmes should be regularly reviewed and their effectiveness fully evaluated. Governors, as well as prison medical/nursing staff, need to be aware of the public health concerns which underlie the strategy as well as being committed to the principle of care for the drug misuser in prison.

9 CONCLUSION

9.1 Scotland has a serious drug misuse problem which manifests itself in a variety of ways. In particular the high levels of injecting in Scotland by comparison with the rest of the United Kingdom, and indeed Europe, must be reversed because of the inherent risks of overdosing and death and, when needles are shared, the threat of HIV/AIDS and Hepatitis. This, we believe, can most effectively be tackled by drug misuse services doing all in their power to influence drug misusers to give up injecting; and by harm reduction measures such as the development of structured substitute prescribing arrangements. However, there must also be concern about the almost casual attitude to the use of a range of controlled drugs by many young people in the course of their leisure pursuits. What is required to combat this trend is a cultural change in our young people. If this is to be achieved, we must maintain the distinction between acceptable and unacceptable behaviour which the criminal law provides. Drugs are controlled by the Misuse of Drugs Act because of their harmfulness and adverse social consequences. The effects of drugs on mind and body would not suddenly disappear if legal restrictions were removed. The destructive effects of drug misuse on individuals' families and communities would not evaporate if drugs currently controlled were made freely available. Quite the reverse. The signal would be that drug taking was acceptable. Consequently decriminalisation would inevitably encourage the much wider use of drugs and would expose larger numbers of people, particularly young people, who would be the most likely group to engage in further experimentation, to their harmful effects.

9.2 The key to tackling the drug problem effectively lies in co-ordinated community action, embracing persuasive prevention methods which influence young people's behaviour; in energetic policing to disrupt and arrest those who supply and deal in illicit drugs; and in responsive services which enable those who do misuse controlled drugs to recover as quickly as possible and subsequently remain drug-free. The multi-agency, multi-disciplinary approach necessary to tackle the drugs misuse problem must be driven by effective, dynamic and co-ordinated leadership in a way which secures the 'ownership' of all the agencies and is understood and supported by the community. Much good work is already being done in this difficult and complex area. We have sought in this report to identify how this work can be focussed, developed and taken forward to maximum effect. Good and effective co-operation between the statutory and voluntary bodies at national and local level is essential and the mechanisms which we have recommended should provide a framework for better collaboration.

9.3 In concluding, we wish to emphasise that combating drug misuse is not just the responsibility of the Government or the statutory and voluntary agencies: it is the responsibility of the whole community and only through the community working together will there be any hope of success.

Printed by HMSO Print Centre 10/94 (058942)